The Institute of Biology's
Studies in Biology no. 57

Dormancy and the Survival of Plants

Trevor A. Villiers

Ph.D.

Professor of Biology
University of Natal

Edward Arnold

First published 1975
by Edward Arnold (Publishers) Limited,
25 Hill Street, London W1X 8LL

Board edition ISBN: 0 7131 2516 0
Paper edition ISBN: 0 7131 2517 9

EX LIBRIS

John Hoddinott

Printed in Great Britain by
Butler & Tanner Ltd, Frome and London

General Preface to the Series

It is no longer possible for one textbook to cover the whole field of Biology and to remain sufficiently up to date. At the same time teachers and students at school, college or university need to keep abreast of recent trends and know where the most significant developments are taking place.

To meet the need for this progressive approach the Institute of Biology has for some years sponsored this series of booklets dealing with subjects specially selected by a panel of editors. The enthusiastic acceptance of the series by teachers and students at school, college and university shows the usefulness of the books in providing a clear and up-to-date coverage of topics particularly in areas of research and changing views.

Among features of the series are the attention given to methods, the inclusion of a selected list of books for further reading and, wherever possible, suggestions for practical work.

Readers' comments will be welcomed by the author or the Education Officer of the Institute.

1975

The Institute of Biology,
41 Queens Gate,
London, SW7 5HU

Preface

Climate is the major factor determining plant distribution, and the success of a species in withstanding adverse seasonal conditions has depended upon the evolution of biochemical, physiological and structural adaptations for dormancy. There are many biological advantages to be gained from such adaptations, and it is not surprising that different dormancy mechanisms have evolved in parallel in various groups of organisms. Dormancy is much more than a mere pause in growth. It is a distinct developmental stage in the life cycle which requires the perception and interpretation of environmental signals allowing the synchronization of life processes with the changing seasons.

1975   T.A.V.

Contents

1 The Dormant State

1.1 Introduction

The environment undergoes cyclic changes in which seasons favourable for growth are usually separated by periods when development must be very slow or perhaps entirely suspended, and therefore the success of a species in any habitat depends not only on its successful resistance to adverse climatic conditions, but also on an ability to synchronize its cycles of growth and reproduction with the changing seasons. It is usually essential for an organism to undergo periods of inactivity which may require the formation of special protective structures, and these periods are represented by the several states and degrees of dormancy. The development of dormancy has therefore been a major factor in evolution which has allowed the synchronization of life processes among the members of a population, and between their successive developmental stages and the seasons.

The suspension and re-activation of growth in synchrony with the seasons suggests that signals from the environment can be interpreted and used to control development and metabolism. In plants, periods of intensive growth and reproduction must occur during periods of favourable temperature and water availability. In animals there is in addition the necessity to coincide their activities with the availability of the food species. However, an organism does not become truly dormant in immediate response to a change in the weather, but must sometimes make elaborate preparations for the dormancy state well in advance, allowing time for altered patterns of food storage, for alterations in metabolism to produce new substances, for reproductive structures to be formed, and for developmental processes to be switched to provide protective structures. Because these processes themselves require favourable weather to continue for some time, the signal for preparation for dormancy must be interpreted in most cases before the onset of the adverse conditions themselves, and therefore may not be directly related to them. As the conditions for breaking dormancy may be experienced during the period of adversity, the factor responsible for the relief of the dormant state may be quite different from that stimulating entry into dormancy.

Response to climatic signals may result in the development of cold-hardiness and in a temporary suspension of growth, or may cause a plant to lose part, or even the whole, of its above-ground structures. Developmental pathways may be altered to produce protective bud scales in place of vegetative leaves and to cause a change from vegetative to reproductive growth. The seed habit, one of the most important evolutionary advances in the plant kingdom, requires the property of dormancy to be superimposed upon the primary role of the seed as a structure allowing the dispersal of the species. The reproductive behaviour of most living organisms has become seasonally synchronized, and, in many cases, connected with dormancy in ways which allow maximum benefit to be derived from the period of favourable weather.

Some properties of the dormant state, such as the development of cold-hardiness, tolerance to water loss and responses to similar environmental signals are to be found in a very wide range of living organisms. It is certain that dormancy as a survival mechanism must necessarily have been acquired early in evolution, and the widespread possession of one or other type of dormancy throughout the plant and animal kingdoms emphasizes the fundamental importance to life of climate and seasonal change.

1.2   Defining the dormant state

When an ordinary word is used to describe a natural process, it often becomes loosely applied. Thus the term dormancy is generally used in its broadest sense to describe any state of suspended activity, especially in plants. However, although their growth can be suspended for a time by lowering the temperature, actively growing plants usually become frozen and are killed if the temperature falls much below 0 °C. The same plants, when prepared for winter conditions, may be able to resist temperatures of − 80 °C without freezing or obvious harm. It is therefore evident that true dormancy is a special physiological property, and the term should be used carefully in a scientific context.

Most dormancy states require special environmental conditions for their relief which are different from those imposing dormancy, and may not be conditions which normally support active growth. Many seeds fail to germinate until they have been dried and re-imbibed, or until they have passed through a period of near-freezing weather. Again, the winter buds of temperate-climate trees are formed in conditions which we would imagine should allow continuous growth, and are released from dormancy after experiencing chilling during the winter. It may be concluded that dormancy is a state in which, even though normally favourable conditions of warm temperatures, adequate water and aeration are supplied, growth and development do not take place until a special set of conditions has been experienced.

It can be seen, therefore, that the term 'dormant' should preferably not be applied to dry seeds. When supplied with water, the seeds of many common crop plants begin growth almost immediately and germinate to produce a seedling, and yet these seeds are still said to be 'dormant' in most published biological works. Such seeds may merely be prevented from continuing growth by lack of water. Deep dormancy can be a nuisance to farmers and foresters, who require prompt germination and uniform growth of their crops, and therefore over many generations they have selected seeds possessing these characteristics. The seeds of almost all wild plants, and the majority of recently domesticated ones, possess one or another dormancy-imposing mechanism without which they could not survive in nature.

Some authors, therefore, prefer to distinguish between true dormancy, as defined above, and 'quiescence', which is merely the prevention of growth by the absence of one of the basic conditions for normal growth, such as insufficient water in an air-dry seed (Fig. 1–1). In this

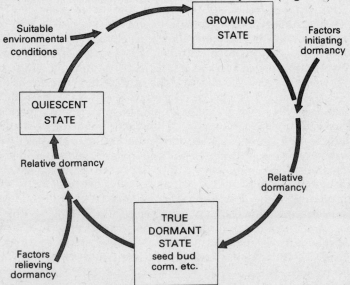

Fig. 1–1 Schematic representation of the cycle of transformations between growth and dormancy

book, the terms dormancy and quiescence will be used where appropriate to the condition according to the definitions given in this section. Because they are economically important and easily available, a great deal of research has been done on the physiology of germination using the quiescent seeds of cultivated crop plants. It is important to remember that these are few compared with the vast majority of species, and because of their lack of true dormancy characteristics, are poorly adapted to survive in nature.

1.3 Dormancy and ecology

In the Introduction it was suggested that the possession of the property of dormancy as a means of avoiding climatic stress has been of great importance in evolution, allowing the colonization of habitats unfavourable for growth at certain times of the year. It is possible for plants to be non-mobile because they are able to make all their food requirements from simple substances obtained from the soil and the air, and therefore the physiology of most plants requires them to live permanently in close association with the soil. However, for a species to be dispersed it is necessary for at least one stage in the life cycle to be mobile, and in order to survive when detached, a transient, water-independent stage is desirable. This requirement is met by the production of spores and seeds, and, since their germination and establishment is the most critical time in the life cycle, means of controlling their time of production and their responses to environmental conditions are essential if the species is to survive.

Plants known as 'winter annuals' are characteristic of areas having hot dry summers and cool wet winters. Their seeds are usually produced and dispersed in the spring and lie dormant throughout the summer when it would be very difficult for a delicate seedling to establish itself on the dry soil surface. It may be thought that this inactivity is directly due to the absence of water, but even if unseasonal rain is experienced, these seeds still do not germinate, but remain dormant until the autumn rains. If the seeds germinated too early, the seedlings produced would be unable to establish themselves in the dry soil, and the whole crop of seeds would die. On the other hand, if the seeds germinated too late in the autumn, they might not become established or develop winter hardiness in time after establishment, and may be killed by the winter frosts. The germination response is, therefore, found to be possible only after a minimal period of dryness has been experienced by the seeds, followed by rain within a certain range of temperatures. This fine control over seed germination allows the species to survive in this particular climatic regime.

The family Caryophyllaceae, which includes the pinks and campions, shows a pattern of germination response to temperature which appears to be correlated with the geographical distribution of species, and which allows the stage of seedling establishment to occur at the most favourable time of year in their particular climatic areas. Species inhabiting the Mediterranean climatic area germinate at cool temperatures, thus allowing the seedling to avoid the hot, dry summer season. Response to a higher temperature range is found in those species of the same family inhabiting the deciduous forest climatic zone, allowing the seedling to become established in summer, when water is not scarce, but delaying the germination of autumn-produced seeds until the following year, thus allowing the very young seedlings to avoid the winter frosts (Fig. 1–2).

In addition to these factors of water and temperature, plants inhabiting climatic regions at different latitudes show responses to the length of the daily cycle of illumination, or photoperiod. The same species develop physiological varieties which make it important to know the place of origin of a batch of seeds. Poplar trees from northern latitudes become dormant in longer days than those of the same species from further south, using daylength as the environmental signal for the approach of winter rather than a lowering of the temperature. Trees grown in northerly latitudes from seeds produced further south do not begin to prepare for winter dormancy until late in the season, when the

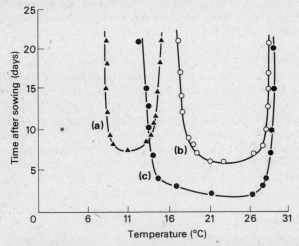

Fig. 1–2 Germination responses of 3 species of Caryophyllaceae to a wide temperature range. The points on each curve represent the maximum and minimum temperatures on successive days at which 50% of the final germination figure was reached. The germination temperature ranges reflect the climates of the areas which the species inhabit (**a**) *Silene secundiflora*, limited to Mediterranean coast; (**b**) *Lychnis flos-cuculi*; widespread except Mediterranean; (**c**) *Silene viscosa*, Central and Eastern Europe. (THOMPSON, P. A. (1970). *Ann. Bot.* **34**, 427)

correct daylength for the variety is experienced, and may be damaged or killed by winter frosts which begin earlier at higher latitudes.

From these few examples, chosen to illustrate some effects of temperature, rainfall and daylength, it can be seen that plant species may be closely adapted to the particular climatic cycle of their habitat. However, it must not be thought that this ecological relationship is static. There is sufficient variability in the responses to climate to allow survival in spite of chance variations in the weather, and it is this variability which presumably has allowed both the spread of species, and also their gradual evolution in response to climate. The occurrence of living organisms in extreme climatic conditions is proof of their great adaptability, in which dormancy plays a most important part.

2 Climate and Survival

In Chapter 1 it was concluded that dormancy is an essential means whereby organisms are able to populate areas which experience adverse climatic changes, and has thus been an important factor in evolution. It may therefore be of interest to survey briefly the causes of the seasonal cycles and their effects on plant life.

2.1 The seasons

The regular changes which constitute the seasons are due to the fact that the earth, in its passage round the sun, has the axis of its own rotation at an angle to the plane of its orbit. Therefore, as the earth travels round the sun, one pole of its axis slopes towards the sun at one part of the year, and away from the sun at the opposite time of the year. Thus the change in the degree of warming between winter and summer at any place is caused chiefly by the varying angle between the sun's rays and the earth's surface caused by this tilt of the axis.

Regions near the equator do not differ much in the amount of heat received at different times of the year, and therefore do not have clearly separate warm and cold seasons, but outside the tropics the climate becomes more markedly seasonal with increasing latitude both to the north and to the south. When the north pole is tilted towards the sun, it is summer for places in the northern hemisphere with its longest day being on 21 June, when the sun is directly overhead at midday at latitude 23.5 °N. The northern hemisphere has its shortest day on 22 December, when the north pole slopes directly away from the sun, which is then overhead at midday at latitude 23.5 °S, giving midsummer in the southern hemisphere (Fig. 2–1).

The earth's tilt is therefore responsible for the changes in heating of its surface and therefore also for the seasonality of its climates. It is also responsible for the very strict regularity of the changes in daylength experienced everywhere on earth. At midsummer, places north of the latitude 23.5 °N experience their longest day and shortest night. From this day onwards, as the sun appears to move lower across the sky each day, the days become shorter until the earth's axis is pointing neither away from nor towards the sun, which happens twice during each yearly orbit, giving days and nights of equal length everywhere on earth. After the autumn 'equinox', the day becomes increasingly shorter than the night until midwinter. The seasonal daylength changes are exactly the opposite for places south of latitude 23.5 °S. At regions north of latitude 66.5 °N and south of 66.5 ·S, called the Arctic and Antarctic circles, there

is a period of continuous illumination during their respective summers
and of continuous darkness in their winters the duration of which increases with the latitude.

It might at first be thought that the hottest and coldest days of the
year at any place would be the longest and shortest days respectively.
However, the amount of heat at any one place is a compromise between
the amount received daily from the sun and the amount radiated away.
The rate of radiation is greater the higher the ground temperature, and
although by midsummer the amount of heat received daily is greatest,
the ground has not yet warmed up sufficiently to radiate away as much
heat as it receives. This causes a distinct lag in the timing of the highest

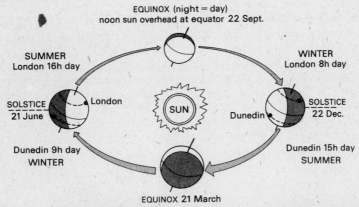

Fig. 2–1 Seasonal changes through the year, showing the differences in daylength due to the tilt of the earth's axis of rotation relative to the plane of its
orbit round the sun

ground temperature which in turn affects the air temperature, and the
warmest time of the year in the northern hemisphere therefore occurs
later than midsummer's day, being more than a month late in the maritime climate of Western Europe (see Fig. 2–3). In the same way, there
is a lag in the lowest average yearly temperature, which occurs considerably later than the shortest day. It is therefore important to note that
in summer the daylengths become shorter even while the temperatures
continue to rise, and have become considerably shorter by the time the
temperatures have fallen sufficiently to begin to curtail metabolism.
This point will be returned to in Chapter 5.

2.2   Climate

The word climate is derived from the Greek word meaning a slope
and refers to the angle of the sun's inclination, which varies in a precise
manner with the time of year. The amount of heat received at any place

is directly related to this angle and therefore to latitude, and is the basic factor determining climate (Fig. 2–2). However, many other factors combine to affect the temperature of a particular area, including the speed and direction of the wind, the humidity, the rainfall, the proximity of the sea and the topography of the land, and their combined effects constitute the climate of an area.

The water-holding capacity of the air varies with its temperature, and therefore atmospheric humidity depends on air temperature and rainfall depends on changes in the air temperature. The heat of the tropics becomes distributed over the rest of the earth partly by ocean currents and partly by wind. Due to the unequal heating of the earth's surface, the atmosphere tends to flow from one place to another, creating the major wind systems. Warm winds pick up evaporated moisture as they pass over the oceans, and precipitate this as rainfall either in cooler areas or when forced to rise and so become cooler, either on meeting a 'cold front' or when moving against a mountain range. In this latter case the windward side of a mountain can experience a wet climate while the leeward side can lie in a 'rain shadow', and may constitute a desert.

Air is not warmed by the passage of sunlight through it, but from

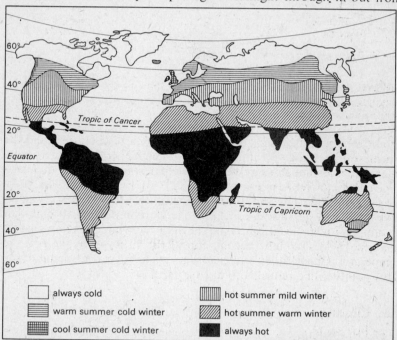

Fig. 2–2 The general pattern of climatic zones roughly follows the lines of latitude, being basically dependent upon the heating effect of the sun. However, there are many local disturbing influences (SMITH, 1970)

Table 1   World climatic zones described by vegetation type

World Climatic Zones		
A. Tropical rainy climates	1.	Tropical rain forest
	2.	Savanna
B. Dry climates	3.	Steppe
	4.	Desert
C. Temperate forest climates	5.	Warm, with dry winter
	6.	Warm, rain throughout year
	7.	Warm, with dry summer
D. Snow-forest climates	8.	Snow forest, rain at all seasons
	9.	Snow forest, with dry winter
E. Polar climates	10.	Tundra
	11.	Perpetual snow and ice

contact with the water or the soil which absorbs the sun's rays. The land warms up more quickly than the sea, and also cools more quickly, the sea retaining its heat for a longer period. Consequently, the atmosphere over the sea, and over land in its vicinity, does not undergo such wide temperature variations as does the air over a continental land mass, and the climates of islands and coastal areas are far more equable than those of central continental regions (Fig. 2–3). In addition, there may be a further effect caused by warm or cold water currents passing along a coastline. Both the Gulf Stream current and the prevailing south-westerly winds which have passed over the Atlantic combine to give Britain an equable climate for its northerly latitude, with a relatively small annual range of warm temperature. It is interesting to note

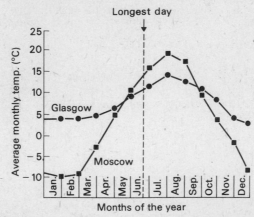

Fig. 2–3   Comparison of the seasonal temperature ranges of Glasgow (maritime climate) and Moscow (continental climate). Note that the maximum annual temperatures occur well after the longest day

that Glasgow lies at the same latitude as Moscow, which has a relatively large range of annual temperature.

Because so many factors combine in such complex ways to affect the weather experienced in any area, it is difficult to obtain a useful classification of climates. However, plants appear to be so dependent upon climate that major types of vegetation can be distinguished, and have been used as visible indicators in naming and mapping climatic areas. Such a system is useful since it relates to agricultural potential and therefore directly to human economy.

2.3   Daylength, temperature and water

It may be concluded that the majority of factors affecting climate are largely unpredictable and therefore not reliable as markers of the seasonal cycles. It is especially undesirable to use the general trend of falling temperature as a signal of the approach of winter, because time is still required after receipt of the signal in order to make adequate preparations for withstanding the adverse season. It might be thought that annually-cycling rhythms of activity, which occur as part of the physiology of organisms, would be all that is required, but there is no doubt that the innate variability of living things in time puts all such rhythms badly out of step. It is therefore obviously desirable to have some accurate means of synchronizing rhythms of annual growth and reproductive activity, and this is provided by the daylength which varies in a predictable and highly regular manner at all places on earth (Fig. 2–4).

In general, plants of the tropics and sub-tropics respond to cycles of alternation of light and dark where the day never becomes very long nor the night very short, and plants of the temperate regions respond to daily light–dark cycles where at certain seasons the daylength far

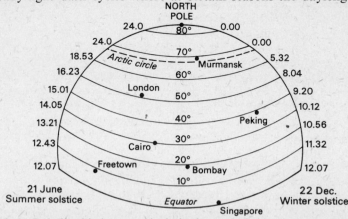

Fig. 2–4   Relationship between the latitude north of the equator and the daylengths in summer (left) and winter (right) recorded in hours

exceeds the length of darkness. This distinction between so-called 'short-day' and 'long-day' plants is not necessarily species-specific, since the same species can possess both long and short-day races according to its distribution over the latitudes. It is an important factor to be considered in the introduction of new types of plants into a country. A good example of such a response to daylength is found in the tea plant, which grows throughout the year near the equator, but outside the tropics enters complete winter dormancy, thus greatly decreasing the total yield of the crop. Increasing the length of day from 11 to 13 hours breaks this dormancy and allows growth of the winter buds, but the stimulus is not one of additional food being available from photosynthesis, since the extra period of illumination can be given merely by switching on a few electric lamps among the plants, giving less than 1% of the normal sunlight intensity. The measurement of daylength can be quite accurate: tropical trees living within 8 °N of the equator have been shown to be capable of distinguishing the small differences in daylength occurring annually at that latitude.

Because temperature influences the moisture-holding capacity of the air and therefore the rainfall, the amount of water available to terrestrial plants is to a large extent dependent upon temperature. In general, the metabolism of living organisms follows the chemical rule that the rate of a reaction increases with rise in temperature. Therefore the growth rates of plants, which have little control over their tissue temperatures, would be expected to depend directly upon temperature. Low temperatures not only slow down metabolism but can be physically damaging through freezing the tissues. Many plants are adapted to withstand extremes of climate, and where winter temperatures are very low, or where water becomes scarce, they may lose parts of their aerial structures, or die off altogether to leave only seeds to carry on the life cycle. Some idea of the importance of temperature to plant growth can be seen in the establishment of a 'tree line' as the most northerly limit of tree growth, or the highest limit of tree growth on a mountain.

Whereas daylength is used as a predictable and accurate signal of seasonal change, the total length of winter chilling is frequently also used as a measure of time to indicate that winter is past. It would be undesirable for a mere rise in temperature to signal the approach of spring, as growth would sometimes begin far too early after an unseasonable warm spell and the plant would then begin growth and lose its cold-hardiness, and therefore many species of temperate climate plants can be shown to require a minimal period of chilling at about 5 °C before they subsequently begin to grow at warm temperatures. Thus, it is frequently found that after a mild winter, in spite of the coming of good growing conditions, buds and seeds may not be fully released from dormancy and growth may be slow and abnormal. Fruit farmers are well aware of the ability of deciduous trees to assess the winter conditions while dormant and apparently insensitive. Thus, day-length and temperature may act at different parts of the annual growth cycle to signal changes in the seasons.

In many parts of the tropics, the temperature may be sufficiently high to permit growth at all times of the year. Even in the tropical forest, however, although the leaves may remain on plants the whole year round, growth of the stems and the formation of new leaves usually occurs in cycles corresponding to seasonal growth. In many warm areas, growth may be prevented by seasonal dryness and plants meet this in

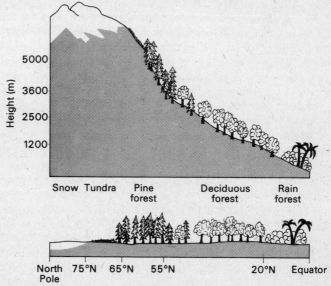

Fig. 2–5   General comparison between latitude and altitude in their support of vegetation

much the same way as they prepare for winter cold, by existing as leafless aerial parts, as underground structures, and as seeds.

There is a further relationship between cold and the availability of water, which may become seasonally unavailable to the plant when present as ice or snow. Even cold water presents a problem in being viscous and offering a greater resistance to uptake by root systems. Thus it may happen that although leaf temperatures may be sufficiently high to cause rapid loss of water into the air, the soil temperature may be too low to allow rapid replacement of the water lost, and large water deficits may be caused in plants, e.g. conifers, in cold temperate climate forests in winter. Snow is not necessarily harmful, however, as it affords a protective insulating blanket over the ground, retarding heat loss from radiation. Under snow cover, soil temperatures may remain close to freezing point, allowing the survival of underground organs, even though outside air temperatures are extremely low.

3 Structural Modifications in Dormancy

3.1 Bud structure

The growth of plants is confined to certain special zones, including the tips of shoots and roots, known as meristems. These are centres of cell division activity and have high rates of metabolism during active growth. The cell walls are necessarily very thin and the tissue consequently delicate. The shoot meristem gives rise to the aerial organs of the plant such as leaves, the early morphological development of which takes place while they are still appressed over the meristem. The cells forming the stem have not yet undergone extension growth, and therefore the meristem and leaf primordia are protected from excessive water loss and mechanical damage by the series of enclosing young leaves. These centres of organ formation are the buds, which exist throughout the life of the plant, and in perennials usually undergo successive cycles of activity and dormancy.

In the formation of a winter bud, stem cell elongation ceases, and the production of vegetative leaves may change to give rise to a short succession of scales which remain tightly appressed around the bud and by their close-fitting shape and resistant texture, give protection to the over-wintering stem tip (Fig. 3–1). After the requisite number of scales has been formed, the meristem immediately continues to form a succession of vegetative leaf or flower primordia, which remain within the

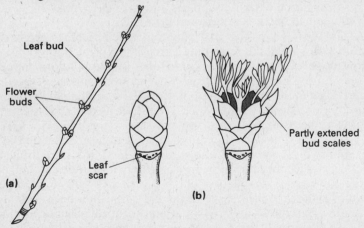

Fig. 3–1   Winter buds. (a). Dormant peach twig, showing leaf and flower buds. (b) Winter terminal bud and out-growing shoot of horse-chestnut

winter bud as miniature organs, growing out only after release of the entire bud from winter dormancy. In some species, all the leaves which will function during the next season are pre-formed in the winter bud (see Fig. 5–1).

Instead of an abrupt change, some plants show a gradual transition in morphology from leaf to bud scale and back to vegetative leaf. Again, dormant buds are not always enclosed by distinctly modified bud scales, but in some species only the young undeveloped leaves remain appressed round the tip of the shoot during the period of dormancy. This kind of bud is often found in shrubs and non-woody over-wintering plants, and it is therefore evident that although of protective value, the formation of completely modified bud scales is not essential for survival of the bud in winter. The winter buds of many plants are not completely inactive, and slow differentiation of the internal organs can take place except in the very coldest weather.

3.2   Rhizomes, bulbs and other dormant organs

Underground stems are produced by many plants and although they may appear superficially very different from aerial shoots, sometimes they are modified little except in their habit of growth. Underground stems are usually formed by plants which die back to soil level in pre-paration for the winter or a dry season. A rhizome is an underground horizontally-growing stem which has buds and reduced scale leaves. It either grows above the soil by vertically-growing branches, or itself turns upwards to the surface, in which case underground growth is con-tinued from one or more branches. Food is stored in the rhizome during the growth period of the aerial parts and is used to make rapid aerial growth after the period of seasonal dormancy.

A stem tuber is a distinct part of a stem which becomes swollen into a storage organ, all the remaining parts of the plant both above and below the soil dying back. The potato tuber is a deeply-dormant organ formed during one growing season as an over-wintering vegetative organ. Each of the 'eyes' of the potato is the scar of a small scale leaf bearing a rudimentary bud, which grows out as a branch stem from the tuber after winter.

A corm is a squat highly-reduced stem, vertically orientated in the soil, and swollen laterally in the storage of food. Buds are formed on its upper surface and, after growing upwards to form the new plant early in the growing season, the base of the new shoot swells to form a new corm over the shrivelled tissue of the old corm. In a bulb such as the hyacinth, the stem is similarly squat and vertically orientated but the function of food storage is taken over by the bases of the leaves, all of which arise in very close succession on the modified basal stem and become thick and fleshy. Modified roots also serve as dormant, over-wintering organs, such as the tap root of the carrot, and the spindle-shaped root tubers of the dahlia plant. After these various vegetative organs are formed in response to environmental signals they remain dormant for various periods of time and are released from dormancy after a minimal period of inactivity, sometimes more rapidly at cool, but not freezing, temperatures (see Fig. 9–2).

The complete loss of aerial parts is not necessary as a climatic stress-avoidance mechanism, since many plants, such as conifers and even the delicate-looking birch and willow trees, survive under very severe climatic stress. The existence of plants in the far north seems to be controlled rather by the length of the season available for growing, together with its temperature range, rather than by the extreme cold or drought of the winter season. The formation of bulbs, corms and rhizomes as underground structures might be admirable ways of over-wintering, but these plant-forms are typical of grassland plant associations where fire is frequently experienced as one of the factors controlling the type of vegetation. Whereas plant parts above ground would be killed during a fire, underground organs are not usually harmed. The underground storage organs of many grassland flowers therefore contain large quantities of quickly-available food, and allow very rapid growth to be made very early in the season, reproduction taking place before the grasses have established a competing cover. The plants then remain alive but inactive during late summer and winter in a dormant state. Thus, the peculiar life form and its associated dormant state have been described as adaptations to a special habitat rather than being climatic adaptations.

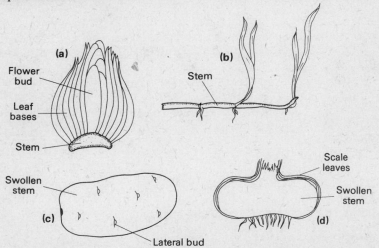

Fig. 3–2   (a) Section through a bulb. (b) Rhizome. (c) Stem tuber. (d) Section through a corm

3.3   Seed structure

The evolution of the seed habit was of great importance, and evidently conferred many advantages in competition, since the seed-bearers have displaced the spore-bearers to become the dominant land plants of today. The way of life of the plant demands that it remains in close association with the substrate on which it grows, and therefore the production of a mobile dispersal unit is important. The seed is sexually produced and therefore a source of genetic variation. Fertilization and early development of the offspring take place on the parent, producing a miniature plant with its own food supply encapsulated as a dispersal unit. Within the seed, the embryo takes on a physiological state of great resistance to adverse conditions, and possesses built-in safeguards of dormancy which allow it to germinate and begin growth again at the most propitious time of the climatic seasonal cycle.

A seed is a mature ovule which has been fertilized and has developed a rudimentary plant (embryo) together with a food supply, the whole being surrounded by protective coats developed from the original walls of the ovule. The embryo consists of an axis (hypocotyl) terminated by a rudimentary root (radicle) and a stem growing point (plumule), and bearing one or more embryonic leaves (cotyledons). The cells of the embryo usually contain a large amount of stored foods such as oil, starch and protein, and the cotyledons may in some species become greatly swollen to accommodate this food, as in the garden pea. In others, such as the castor oil seed, the greater part of the food supply may lie outside the embryo in a tissue formed as one of the products of fertilization (endosperm) (Fig. 3–3). In the flowering plants, one or

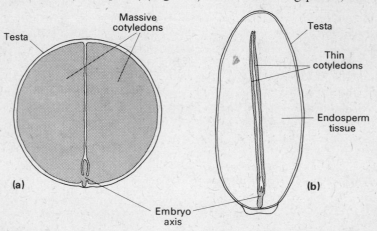

Fig. 3–3   Seed structure. (a) Non-endospermous seed of pea, with massive food-storing cotyledons. (b) Seed of castor oil plant, with thin embryo embedded in food-storing endosperm tissue

more ovules are enclosed within a container (ovary), which after pollination of the flower may develop in a remarkable variety of ways into the fruit wall. Thus a fruit encloses one or more seeds which have developed from the ovules which it originally contained. In many cases the seeds are dispersed separately, but in others, such as the grasses, the fruit is one-seeded and is dispersed as an entire unit. The wheat grain is therefore not really a seed but an entire fruit containing a single seed.

Although the seed is not unique in being able to become air-dry and yet remain alive, this special ability is a remarkable property. Not all seeds lose water to the point where they are in equilibrium with the humidity of the air. Some species, such as citrus, are actually damaged by becoming air-dry, while the seeds of some fleshy fruits probably lose very little water in natural conditions. Whereas a few species such as clover rely upon a low water content for maintenance of their inactive, non-growing state, it is likely that the majority of seeds are dry for only a short period of time, as they mature and are dispersed, but after falling onto the surface of the soil, or into the surface litter, they soon become re-imbibed with water, the hygroscopic nature of their colloidal contents ensuring that they remain well hydrated whenever water is available from rain, dew, or the soil. However, in spite of being hydrated, the seeds of wild plants do not germinate immediately but remain dormant until certain conditions have been fulfilled. Even in dry seeds most of the normal cellular structures can still be recognized microscopically. The cells appear collapsed, but the normal structure is regained very quickly when water is imbibed.

Thus the seed provides genetic variability together with continuity from generation to generation. It allows species dispersal in a highly protected form, together with a food supply for the pre-formed young plant and a means of timing of the commencement of the critical early stages of its establishment. Seeds have always been of the greatest importance to Man, and it is certainly no coincidence that the centres of development of the great civilizations coincide with the areas of origin of the major grain crops, as seeds constitute by far the largest source of food supply in the most convenient form for storage.

4 Resistance of Dormant Organisms

Dormant organisms are typically highly resistant to adverse environmental conditions, microbial attack and even irradiation. Many organisms become greatly modified morphologically, chemically and physiologically in preparation for the dormant state, as in the formation of cysts, spores, buds and seeds. However, while such modifications may be highly protective and therefore of survival value, they are not necessarily a pre-requisite for resistance to adverse conditions. Lower plants such as the mosses, and higher plants such as the resurrection plant can lose water and become highly resistant, and pond-inhabiting larvae of some insects can undergo desiccation and resist great extremes of temperature, and yet can resume feeding within one hour of being rehydrated. However, while being of great interest, they are not true dormancy states, which may or may not involve drying out but always involve some block to growth imposed by the organisms themselves. As dormancy is primarily a stress-avoidance mechanism, resistance to adverse conditions would be expected to be one of its most important properties.

Table 2 The term hypobiosis describes potentially viable states of inactive organisms, and is sub-divided as follows (KEILIN, D. (1959). *Proc. Roy. Soc., London.* B150. 149)

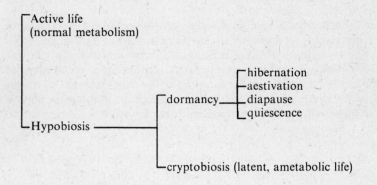

4.1 Resistance to desiccation

The ability to exist as a latent form of life while in the dry state is termed anhydrobiosis. Many, but by no means all dormant organisms are able to tolerate a low water content either as a mechanism for resistance to some specific environmental extreme, as in the seeds of flowering annual plants of the desert regions, or merely as a short-term resistance during the period of seed dispersal. Whereas actively-growing plant tissues may contain 80 to 90% of their total tissue weight as water, many seeds in nature may possess as little as 10% water, and in artificial storage, may achieve their greatest longevity at about 5% water content. Bacterial spores can even be rendered totally anhydrous by freeze-drying and still survive, but seeds appear to have a lower limit beyond which further drying causes damage. However, seeds in natural situations never experience a totally dry atmosphere and therefore this is not a disadvantage. The intact, undamaged seed coats appear to be able to protect against rapid changes in seed moisture content during the changes in humidity which occur daily, and seeds with damaged coats do not survive very long in store unless the humidity is controlled.

Not all the members of a batch of spores or seeds survive desiccation. The rate of drying, the temperature during drying and the presence of certain protective substances such as colloids all affect the retention of viability in the dried organism. In general, lower temperatures are more favourable, which is probably why freeze-drying is possible, and why seeds dried by heating seldom survive. Very rapid drying, and also rapid re-hydration, can sometimes cause cell membranes to burst, releasing the cytoplasm and causing cell death.

Many seeds actually require to become air-dry for a time before they will germinate successfully. This is a dormancy-imposing mechanism found especially in plants which inhabit climatic areas with hot dry seasons, where seeds which germinate immediately would have great difficulty in becoming established. Fig. 4–1 shows this effect in seeds of the winter annual Veronica arvensis.

It is not known conclusively whether air-dry seeds are non-metabolic, or merely have a greatly reduced rate of metabolism. Slow gas exchange can be detected in dry-stored seeds, but this may be due to the presence of micro-organisms growing on the seeds, and perhaps also to chemical oxidation which is not connected with life processes. Reports of enzyme activity in dry seeds are few and conflicting. It is probable that, depending on the amount of water actually present in the tissues, enzyme action is stopped owing to the difficulty of diffusion of the substrates and re-action products.

As water is lost from drying tissues, the physical state of the remaining water changes. When free water is present, the cytoplasm may be said to be in the solution state, and diffusion and enzyme activities can presumably occur normally. As the water is removed by drying, the cell colloids enter a gel state, in which diffusion and transport are impeded. Further drying removes all water except that which is physically adsorbed to the colloidal substances in the seeds. Water is still present, but in an immobile, probably para-crystalline state tightly bound to the macromolecules and free diffusion probably does not occur. Hence enzyme action is prevented and normal metabolism impossible.

4.2 Seed storage

A seed contains a well-balanced diet of food, concentrated and neatly packaged by Nature. The food is used for all the early growth of the young plant and must therefore contain substances, including proteins, carbohydrates, oils, vitamins and minerals, which are also essential to

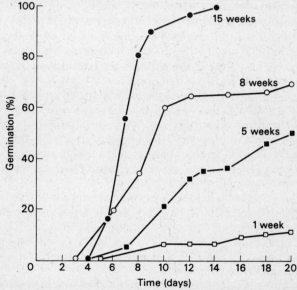

Fig. 4–1 Effect of increasing time of dry storage on the germination of seeds of *Veronica arvensis* at 15 °C. Each curve represents a germination test on a seed sample stored for the number of weeks indicated (JANSSEN, J. (1973). *Oecologia*, **12**, 141)

our own growth, although not necessarily complete or in the correct proportions. Becoming dry at maturity, seeds are light in weight and deteriorate very slowly. Thus, seeds are extremely useful to Man, and it is considered that civilization did not become possible until he learned to cultivate the grain crops.

Seed storage has therefore been one of our main activities and today is a highly-developed technology, supporting the food industry, agriculture, and many manufacturing industries. When used as a food source, the main concern is to keep the seed free from microbial and animal pests. However, when it is to be used for growing more crops, it has also to be kept alive in a genetically stable state.

The first and most important requirement is to keep the seeds at a

low and constant moisture content. Seeds do not remain viable for very
long in equilibrium with ordinary atmospheric humidity, except in certain very dry regions. Modern methods of storage and distribution of
seeds for sowing include artificial drying to a low moisture content and
then hermetic sealing in tins or foil packages so that moisture is not
taken up again from the air. The second requirement is cool temperature, and a well-run seed store is usually air-conditioned, which reduces
both the humidity and the temperature. Composition of the storage
atmosphere is also important, as the viability of a batch of seeds is
greatly extended if oxygen is excluded, probably because non-metabolic
oxidation processes are slowed down.

Table 3   The effect of moisture content and storage temperature on viability
of cotton seeds (from SIMPSON, D. M. (1942). *J. Agric. Res.*, **64**, 407)

% moisture content	% germination after following numbers of years						
	1	2	3	5	7	13	15
Stored at 0.5 °C							
7	87	87	87	90	94	90	91
11	89	88	91	79	89	88	93
14	88	90	85	61	34	10	0
Stored at 21 °C							
7	93	91	90	84	89	85	73
11	86	89	68	1	0	0	0
14	17	0	0	0	0	0	0

Apart from obvious damage due to insect and rodent pests and spoil-
age due to fungus growth, seeds slowly degenerate spontaneously and
accumulate serious damage to their cellular structures and genetic
material which reduces the growth vigour of the subsequent crop, and
which eventually kills the seeds. Most seeds used in agriculture are not
kept longer than one season, and such damage does not become
serious in good conditions. However, for long-term storage, genetic
deterioration is a serious problem because seeds are only usually kept
for very long periods because of the value to plant breeders of their
particular genetic constitutions. It is most useful to be able to keep valuable genetic material in a state of suspended animation, so that newly-
developed crop plants can be crossed back to old stocks when desirable.
Most advanced countries now possess special 'seed banks' where plant
breeders can store valuable seeds under optimum conditions for very
prolonged life.

Moreover, breeders frequently require to obtain samples of the wild
relatives of crop plants for cross-breeding, in order to incorporate some

especially useful property into the progeny, e.g. resistance to a disease. Regrettably, it is becoming increasingly difficult to obtain truly wild relatives of the crop plants owing to the spread of efficient methods of agriculture, and few really wild areas are left in the world today. Therefore specimens of the seeds of wild plants thought to be useful are being collected by government agriculture departments for very long-term storage in seed banks.

4.3   Tolerance of temperature extremes

In general, active growth and metabolism are only possible within a relatively narrow range of temperatures, the upper limit of which is probably set by the stability to heat of proteins and nucleic acids, and the lower limit by the lower rate of chemical reaction as the freezing point is approached. In addition to slowing the rates of reactions, most tissues are easily damaged by the freezing of their contained water, which expands and may disrupt the cellular organization, bursting the cells in the same way that water pipes may burst on freezing.

The effect of adding solutes to water in order to lower its freezing point is well known, as in the case of anti-freeze put in motor car radiators in cold climates, and the same principle is used by plants and animals which have to withstand cold winters. In preparation for dormancy, foods are stored in the tissues. The sugars and other soluble substances effectively lower the freezing point, and more sugar can be mobilized by the conversion of stored polysaccharide in response to a lowering of the temperature. This can be demonstrated simply by keeping potatoes or carrots in a refrigerator for a time, after which they taste noticeably sweeter than stocks kept at room temperatures. Insects use exactly the same method of anti-freeze, and an insect exposed to the correct daylength signal begins to increase the amount of glycerol in its tissues and thereby becomes able to withstand low winter temperatures without freezing solid.

Resistance to extreme temperatures can be placed under two headings. Those organisms which reduce their water content to a low level, such as spores and seeds, and those which become resistant even while their cytoplasm is fully hydrated. It is always found that dried tissues have a remarkable capacity to withstand extremes of temperature, no doubt because their macromolecules have a greatly increased stability when free water is removed. In the air-dry state, many tissues can be subjected to boiling water and to liquid helium ($-270\,°C$) and still recover. However, such resistance can have little selective value since organisms are unlikely to experience such extremes in Nature.

In the second category, the resistance of non-dried tissues to temperature extremes is most interesting. Tissues with a high rate of growth and metabolism do not appear to be able to tolerate rapid temperature changes very successfully, and the sudden exposure of actively-growing organisms to sub-zero temperatures in most cases results in freezing of the tissues and death. Adequately-prepared organisms, on the other hand, are able to tolerate the lowest temperatures found in Nature and still recover. Northern hemisphere trees which would be killed around freezing point in July can withstand more than $-80\,°C$ in winter (see Table 4).

Although winter dormancy is usually broken by chilling, it is noteworthy that temperatures below freezing point are not effective in dormancy-breaking. Temperatures around $5\,°C$ are the most effective and therefore some chemical changes are probably involved. Periods of exposure to about $5\,°C$ are cumulative until the minimal chilling requirement is complete. When dormancy is broken and growth begins again, the seedling or young shoot has a very high rate of metabolism,

Table 4 Relationship between the northerly limit of tree growth and freezing resistance of winter buds (data from SAKAI, A., and WEISER, C. J. (1973). *Ecology*, **54**, 123)

Species	Approximate northern limit (latitude)	Average minimum temperature at northern limit (°C)	Freezing resistance in °C
Oak	32 °N	-4 to -8	-7 to -8
Magnolia	35 °N	-9 to -12	-15 to -20
Liquidamber	40 °N	-18 to -20	-25 to -30
Poplar	48 °N	-32 to -34	below -80
Willow	48 °N	-32 to -34	below -80
Elm	52 °N	-37 to -46	-40 to -50
Birch	60 °N	below $-46\,°C$	below $-80\,°C$

and immediately loses its cold-hardiness. Hence, in many species, there is a further requirement for a minimal period of reasonably warm temperatures after chilling, thus ensuring that the organism does not immediately respond to a day or two of unseasonal warm weather by beginning growth and then being damaged by a return to cold conditions.

4.4 Radiation resistance

Increased resistance to radiation is a further example of the hardiness of dormant organisms. Nucleic acids absorb ultra-violet light energy, and hence u.v. irradiation, including that present as a component of normal sunlight, can cause genetic damage. In the normal course of events this damage is mostly repaired by enzymes present in the nucleus. Micro-organisms are susceptible to various forms of irradiation, and therefore u.v. light is frequently used as a surface-sterilizing agency, whilst ionizing radiation such as gamma-rays are used as a means of sterilizing foods and medical supplies owing to their deep penetration.

Ionizing radiation causes damage, not by preferential absorption into important molecules such as DNA, but by direct damage by ionizing the molecules as the rays pass through, and also indirectly by the ionization of the water surrounding the macromolecules.

Dormant organisms are sometimes highly resistant to irradiation, especially if their water content is reduced as a means of achieving dormancy. As in the case of resistance to extremes of temperature, the macromolecules seem to be more stable when free water is removed from the cells (Fig. 4–2). However, even when dormant tissues remain fully hydrated, there seems to be a greatly increased resistance to radiation and this is usually ascribed to the fact that cell division does not occur during dormancy. Dividing cells are more susceptible to irradiation than non-dividing cells, and this is the basis for the use of ionizing radiation in the treatment of cancer, which is characterized by rapid, apparently uncontrolled cell division. In many dormant tissues the DNA is in the non-replicated part of the cell cycle, that is, the cells have not yet duplicated their chromosomes and so offer a smaller 'target' for the randomly-passing radiation tracks.

In short, resistance to radiation of dormant organisms appears to be partly a physical effect of stabilizing the macromolecules, partly a statistical effect of decreasing the number of target macromolecules, and partly a physiological effect of the relative sensitivity of cellular processes, such as cell division, to its effects.

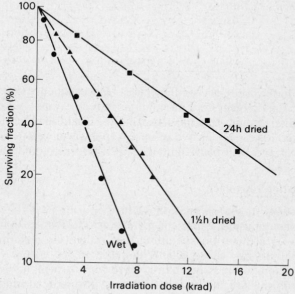

Fig. 4–2 Inactivation of coli bacteria by ionizing radiation at differing degrees of hydration. After drying, the bacteria have an increasing resistance to radiation (BHATTACHARJEE, S. (1961). *Radiation Res.*, **14**, 50)

5 Control of Entry into Dormancy

5.1 The physiology of bud formation

The events leading to the formation of winter buds in perennial plants have been demonstrated in some detail, mainly due to the work of P. F. Wareing and his associates. Winter buds are formed long before the onset of winter while the plant is still experiencing weather conditions suitable for growth. The controlling stimulus has been shown to be the shortening length of day to which mature leaves are exposed, irrespective of the daylength to which the shoot apex itself might be subjected. In some species, such as the oak tree, the shoots form winter buds and cease to grow even if the plant is held in continuous long days, and it is therefore possible that there exists an innate periodicity of cycles of growth and dormancy which are entrained and synchronized by seasonal changes such as daylength and winter temperature.

After exposure to critical daylength cycles, the developmental pattern in the shoot meristems becomes switched from the production of vegetative leaves to the production of a series of bud scales. Further elongation of the stem is prevented, but cell division and morphogenesis continue, providing a series of miniature vegetative leaves or flowers, which remain tightly enclosed by the bud scales (Fig. 5–1).

It should be emphasized that short days do not suspend growth or metabolism, but change pathways of development, and for a time actually *increase* the rate of cell division and the morphogenesis of new organs. Further, in their morphology, anatomy, metabolism and functions, the new bud scales are quite different from the vegetative leaves produced by the same apex previously. Thus, far from merely stopping growth and metabolism, the environmental signal sets in motion a chain of events leading to the switching of development, causing an intensive preparation both for the winter resting state and also for the new spring growth. Only after this does the bud enter a period of low metabolic status until the winter chilling relieves this state of dormancy and permits the resumption of rapid extension growth.

This period of intensive preparation for dormancy is of fundamental importance to the plant, enabling it to enter the winter season in a state resistant to adverse conditions. However, all this activity requires the continuation of favourable weather for some time after receipt of the signal. It has therefore been necessary for the plant to develop responsiveness to a reliable 'early warning system' which allows the necessary changes to be completed before the onset of winter. In addition to the absolute regularity of the timing of daylength cycles, this is the reason why the signal which the plant uses is one of daylength rather than low temperature.

It will be remembered from Section 2.1 that the optimum temperatures for metabolism occur after daylength begins to shorten, and that the daylengths have become considerably shorter by the time temperatures have dropped sufficiently to curtail metabolism. Even in those species which have been shown to possess innate dormancy/growth cycles, the various environmental signals most certainly serve to 'entrain' and synchronize the phases of the rhythm. Changes in daylength can be measured with great accuracy by many plants and animals, and sensitivity to a change of 15 minutes in daylength can be shown in some trees.

In addition to the important morphological changes described above, the general physiology of the whole plant becomes changed during these

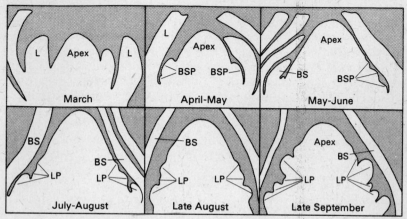

Fig. 5–1 Vertical sections of vegetative shoot apices of Douglas fir at different times during the annual growth cycle. Note that the next season's leaf primordia are formed by the end of the growing season (Sept.) and have developed further (March) during the winter. L, young leaves; LP, leaf primordia; BS, bud scales; BSP, bud scale primordia (Drawn after OWENS, J., and MOLDER, M. (1973). *Canad. J. Bot.*, **51**, 1395)

preparations for winter. Carbohydrates and lipids are stored in the parenchyma cells, and cell walls become strengthened by the production of extra lignin. The pattern of enzyme synthesis changes, and in addition, the plant gradually develops a resistance to low temperatures by the increase of solutes within its tissues.

The transmission of the stimulus from the mature leaves, which are sensitive to photoperiod, to the responding shoot apex is of great interest. In the early stages of investigation it was shown that a seasonal cycle of growth-promoting and growth-inhibiting substances occurred in the twigs of the sycamore tree (*Acer pseudoplatanus*) the activity of the inhibiting substances being high in autumn and winter and low in spring and summer. It was assumed that this extension-growth inhibitor was a dormancy-inducing substance, and it was later shown to be pro-

Table 5 Environmental signals involved and changes caused in preparation for, and release from winter dormancy in woody plants (adapted from PERRY, T. O. (1971). *Science, N.Y.,* **171**, 29)

Shortening daylength *High day/low night temperatures* *Nutrient/water availability*	*Chilling treatment* *Lengthening days*

Increase dormancy-inducing hormone
Stop cellulose synthesis
Increase lignin/starch synthesis
Accumulate lipids/phenols
Change pattern of enzyme synthesis
Stop cambial activity
Initiate bud scales and
    flower/leaf bud formation
Abscission layer in petioles
Develop cold hardiness
	Decrease inhibitors and phenols
	Increase in growth hormones
	Utilization of stored lipids
	Changed pattern of enzyme
	    synthesis
	Increase in respiration
	Cell extension begins
	Cambial activity begins
	Loss of cold hardiness

duced in the mature leaves and transported to the rest of the plant probably through the phloem.

From this growth-inhibiting fraction, a substance was isolated and purified, and shown to be identical with abscisin, which previously had been demonstrated to cause leaf and fruit fall in the cotton plant. The name 'abscisic acid' was eventually decided upon, and many biologists still refer to this as an inhibitor, or as an inhibiting hormone. However, when the biological effect of this substance in the switching of developmental pathways is realized, it can be seen that its action is more positive than would be expected of a mere inhibitor. Because it is produced in one organ, the leaf, following the receipt of an environmental signal, and is transported to affect development and metabolism in another organ, the stem apex, abscisic acid is a hormone both in its function, and by definition.

As the plant does not enter a state of rest immediately upon receipt of the short day signal, but passes through a sequence of changes culminating in rest, it is not surprising to find that the process can be reversed in its earlier stages. Damage to woody plants, either by pruning or defoliation by insect attack, can cause the terminal bud to enter a second 'flush' of growth in the same season. However, the bud normally gradually enters a refractory period of deep dormancy, from which it requires a different stimulus for its release, namely, the climatic stimulus of chilling. The plant is not completely non-metabolic during the refractory period as the roots can still grow, and both morphological and developmental changes can take place slowly inside the winter buds.

5.2 The physiology of seed formation

Whereas a clear picture can be obtained of the events in a shoot from the receipt of an environmental signal to its ultimate effect on developmental processes, the factors which control the induction of dormancy in the seed are unfortunately not known. The embryo within the seed is a young plant of the next generation, but it is completely enclosed by maternal tissues at all stages from its inception at fertilization to maturation of the seed, and is probably influenced by the hormonal status of the parent. The embryo is also at a disadvantage in competition with the surrounding tissues for inwardly-diffusing oxygen, and this may influence its metabolism (Fig. 5–2). However, the primary cause of the changes leading to dormancy in the shoot cannot be due merely to a restriction of oxygen supply to the meristem by the bud scales, since these are the products of the switched pathway.

It has been suggested that dormancy may be controlled by a balance between growth-promoting and dormancy-inducing hormones present in the same organ. Thus, lowering the amount of growth-promoting hormones, or increasing the amount of dormancy-inducing hormone might cause entry into the dormant state, whereas extension growth could be stimulated by the reverse situation. It is interesting to note that in several physiological processes, abscisic acid can be shown to act antagonistically to other plant hormones. The gibberellins (Section 8.4) have been demonstrated to stimulate enzyme production in certain seeds as part of the germination process (Section 9.3), and can promote extension growth when applied to genetically dwarfed or physiologically dwarfed plants. Thus, gibberellin and abscisic acid could represent at least two components of a hormonal system controlling the phases of extension growth and dormancy.

Although at first sight the processes appear to be so different, it should be noted that in the stem apex and also in the embryo, the preparations 'or dormancy involve suppression of cell extension but the continuation ` cell division and morphogenetic activities, and that the reverse pro- c ses of bud break and seed germination are caused in the first instance b ell extension without cell division or morphogenesis. It is therefore

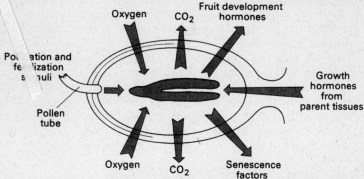

Fig. 5–2 Diagram showing some gradients probably set up between the embryo and its environment in a developing seed

understandable that the same environmental signals, and possibly the same hormonal systems, are involved in controlling dormancy in each case. Temperatures around 5 °C, experienced during winter, break dormancy in both seeds and buds, and the forcing of winter buds and embryos into growth without their chilling requirements being completed results in the remarkably similar symptoms of rosette shoot growth and physiologically dwarfed seedlings, and both states can be relieved either by long-day illumination or by the application of gibberellins (Fig. 5–3).

Whereas most seeds become air-dry for at least a short period of time at maturity, certain species, such as citrus, die if they are allowed to become air-dry. Although seeds are usually imagined as being air-dry non-metabolic systems, it should be remembered that in the majority of species, this condition usually lasts only during dispersal of the seed from the parent plant (Section 6.3). In natural habitats the majority of seeds come to lie in or on the soil in a hydrated state, and remain dormant for a time until they are stimulated to germinate, e.g. by winter chilling. The majority of wild plant seeds possess one or more mechanisms which ensure that they will not germinate until after the seasonal adverse conditions of drought or low temperature have passed, and these will be described in the following section. However, whereas the property of deep dormancy is a nuisance in commercially-grown plants as it spreads the germination of a single batch of seeds over a prolonged period of time, some degree of dormancy is essential, otherwise the embryos would grow continuously and germinate while on the parent plant.

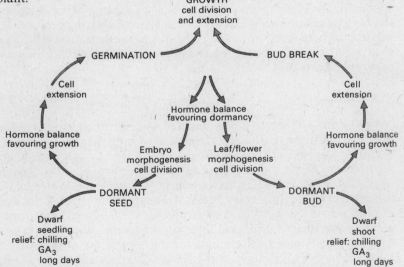

Fig. 5–3 Comparison of some physiological factors involved in the dormancy cycles of seeds and buds

6 Types of Seed Dormancy

In beginning an investigation of a natural phenomenon it is usual to bring the available facts into some kind of order by classification so that common properties and inter-relationships can be seen. In the case of seed dormancy, there have been several attempts at this, and a simple, generally useful classification which is most often used is that of W. Crocker, who described seed dormancy as resulting from; (1) immaturity of the embryo, (2) impermeability of the seed coats to water, (3) mechanical resistance of the seed coats to embryo growth, (4) low permeability of the seed coats to gases, (5) a metabolic block within the embryo itself, requiring (a) light, or (b) chilling for its removal, (6) combinations of the above, and (7) secondary dormancy.

This classification has served well both for research into the dormancy characteristics of many kinds of seeds, and also for the discovery of dormancy-breaking techniques for use in agriculture, horticulture and forestry. The method used in this chapter will be to rearrange the above points into two groups according to whether the state is imposed by the embryo coverings, or is a property of the embryo itself.

6.1 Dormancy imposed by seed coats

In this section are considered those types of seed dormancy which appear to rely solely, or mainly, upon some property of the enclosing seed or fruit coats. This is classed as dormancy rather than quiescence because the state is self-imposed, being due to the structure of the seed itself, rather than a mere prevention of germination by a lack of some environmental factor.

6.1.1 Impermeability of the coats to water

This seems to be one of the simplest and most effective means of delaying the germination of a batch of seeds and of spreading their germination over a period of time. Seeds made dormant by this means are referred to by farmers as 'hard' seeds, and the device is used by several families of plants, including the *Leguminosae*, e.g. clover. Water intake is prevented by the thick-walled cells of the seed testa, which is covered externally by a hard, waxy layer. Rupture of this layer immediately allows water to enter the seed, after which germination soon begins. There is usually much variation in the impermeability of the coats of the seeds in the same batch, and a few seeds are usually able to take up water immediately they fall from the parent plant. The remaining seeds lie without germinating for varying lengths of time, being released by mechanical damage, insect damage, or microbial decomposition of the testa. Many of these hard seeds germinate following a grass fire, since although they are very dry and resistant to high temperatures, the coats become sufficiently damaged to allow water uptake soon afterwards.

Legume seeds which are resistant to water uptake have been shown to possess a modified micropyle which operates a valve-like action, allowing water vapour to diffuse out of the seed in a dry atmosphere, but in a humid atmosphere, or in liquid water, it closes firmly and prevents water entry. Thus the embryo not only remains air-dry, but maintains a very low, steady moisture content, recognized as one of the most important factors in successful seed storage. In agriculture, hard seeds are treated mechanically to scratch the seed coats before they are sown in the soil, and a few minutes soaking in boiling water is also effective in breaking their dormancy, incidentally demonstrating the great resistance of dry seeds to high temperatures.

6.1.2 Impermeability of the coats to gases

The fruit of cocklebur contains two seeds, one dormant and one non-dormant. Removal of the testa from the dormant seed allows its germination, and it has been shown experimentally that pieces of separated testa do not allow oxygen to diffuse through provided they are undamaged. Damage to the seed coats, or increasing the oxygen concentration of the surrounding air allows an increase in the rates of respiration of many kinds of seeds including the grasses, and frequently results in germination (Table 6). In seeds of the apple, the layers surrounding the embryo are thought to restrict its oxygen supply, causing this to be insufficient to maintain the high respiratory activity of the embryo at normal temperatures.

Table 6 Germination percentages of intact fruits and naked seeds of *Fraxinus americana* with intact and damaged coats (VILLIERS, T. A. (1972) *Seed Biology* Vol. 2, 255. Academic Press, New York)

Organ and treatment	% germination (days)			
	2	4	6	8
Intact fruits in air	0	6	10	10
Fruits with pericarps cut	0	12	28	38
Naked seeds in air	0	14	30	42
Seed with testa pricked	14	45	53	53
Seeds in oxygen	40	56	72	78
Seeds pricked, in oxygen	25	62	70	84

6.1.3   Mechanical resistance to embryo growth

This is probably a rare occurrence although many seeds, such as those of the rose, have seeds surrounded by hard, stony layers, and great pressures are needed to destroy them mechanically. However, it has been found that dormancy-imposing hormones are present in rose seeds, and the unchilled embryo may not begin to grow even when removed from its coats. When it is remembered that plants can generate great growth pressures, breaking concrete roadways and lifting paving stones by root growth, it seems unlikely that seeds would be able to restrain an active embryo by this means alone. It is therefore probable that mechanical resistance of seed coats is only one of perhaps several factors operating in a combined dormancy state.

6.2   Embryo dormancy states

Several types of seed dormancy can be shown to be due to a block to metabolism operating within the embryo itself. In some cases even if the embryos of ripe seeds are removed from their enclosing coats and placed in conditions normally found to be suitable for growth, they remain dormant. In other species, although excised embryos may germinate, growth may be unusually slow or abnormal.

6.2.1   Immaturity of the embryo

The embryos of hogweed are rudimentary and undifferentiated when the seeds are mature on the parent plant, and germination is delayed until differentiation is completed. Other species, such as the European ash tree, may have morphologically complete embryos at maturity, but these must still undergo further growth and food accumulation before they are capable of germination. It is frequently found that this type of dormancy is linked with other requirements, such as the necessity for a special temperature range (see Fig. 6–3). As an example, hogweed embryo differentiation takes place at approximately 2 °C rather than at normal growth temperatures. Thus, in such species, the seeds must become imbibed on the ground and remain ungerminated until embryo differentiation is complete, the low temperature requirement allowing embryo maturation during winter.

6.2.2   Requirement for dry storage

Many species of plants produce seeds which will not germinate until the moisture content has been reduced by a period of drying. It offers the greatest advantage where it is necessary for the seedling to avoid a dry season, but is also found in a very wide range of plants. Germination is therefore unlikely to occur while the seeds are still on the parent plant, giving better chances of dispersal and also of survival, because early growth will take place in contact with the soil. Whereas a requirement for a prolonged period of dryness is a disadvantage in agriculture, some degree of dormancy is essential to prevent continuous growth of the embryo on the parent plant. Barley is an example of a plant with a drying requirement under normal conditions, and the seeds must be stored for several months before they can be used, for example in the brewing industry. Temperature, however, affects the response of many such plants, which may not remain dormant if imbibed at lower temperatures (see Fig. 9–1). Thus barley seeds will germinate at 10 °C even when fresh and many crop plants may be ruined by embryo germination on the parent plant itself before harvest if cold rainy weather is experienced during maturation of the crop.

Table 7 Species requiring after-ripening in dry storage and treatment for the relief of dormancy (from BARTON, L. V. (1965). *Handbook of Plant Physiology*, Vol. 15 (2), 699, Springer-Verlag, Berlin)

Species	Period of dry storage	Treatment relieving dormancy
Ambrosia trifida	1–2 years (approx.)	Chilling, 3 months
Cyperus rotundus	7 years	H_2SO_4, 15 minutes
Festuca rubra	1–2 months	Chilling, 7 days
Gossypium hirsutum	1 month	Thorough drying
Hordeum spp.	1½–9 months	Removing hulls
Impatiens balsamina	4–6 months	Chilling, 2 weeks
Lactuca sativa var.		
Grand Rapids	3–9 months	Exposing to light
Lepidium virginicum	2 weeks	Light or KNO_3
Oenothera odorata	7 months	KNO_3
Streptanthus arizonicus	1–2 years	Alternating temperature
Triticum spp.	1–2 months	Pricking coats

6.2.3 Requirement for light

Apart from providing the energy requirement for photosynthesis, light has been shown to control many stages in the development of a plant. The mechanism for the release from dormancy by a light stimulus is similar to that controlling other morphogenetic stages in development, and it was from a study of the photocontrol of germination in lettuce seeds that S. B. Hendricks and H. A. Borthwick obtained the information which led to the discovery of the energy receptor system in light-controlled development (Section 9.1). Many species of plants show this type of dormancy when the seeds are freshly produced, but the requirement for light often disappears during dry storage. Other seeds may become light-requiring if they are allowed to imbibe water in conditions unsuitable for germination, such as an unusual temperature range. Tobacco and certain varieties of lettuce seeds require light, while a few species, such as *Nemophila*, are inhibited by light and germinate better in the dark. Seeds are only sensitive to light when imbibed, and exposure of air-dry seeds has no effect.

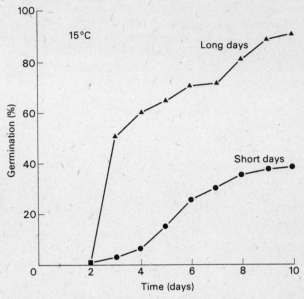

Fig. 6–1   Germination of seeds of the downy birch under long-day illumination cycles (20h light: 4h dark), and short-day cycles (4h light: 20h dark) (BLACK, M., and WAREING, P. F. (1955). *Physiol. Plant.*, **8**, 300)

Apart from a basic requirement for light, an effect of the length of the period of illumination has been shown in several plants, dependent upon the prevailing temperature. Seeds of the downy birch (*Betula pubescens*) require long-day illumination at 15 °C (Fig. 6–1), but at 20 °C will germinate in either long or short days and at 25 °C do not require light at all for germination. Such an apparently odd situation may be related to natural conditions where seeds are caused to remain dormant in winter and early spring when the temperatures are low.

6.2.4   Requirement for chilling

The seeds of a wide range of temperate climate plants require exposure to low temperatures after imbibition. In some cases germina-

tion is merely speeded up, but many species have an absolute requirement for chilling and remain dormant unless exposed to temperatures around 5 °C for a minimal period of time. A similar requirement
is usually shown by the whole plant, which enters a state of winter dormancy relieved by chilling. If the embryos are excised from unchilled
peach or apple seeds and germinated in the laboratory, growth is very
slow and abnormal, with little elongation of the stem internodes, and
distorted leaves. The term 'physiological dwarf' has been used to describe plants showing this condition in order to distinguish it from

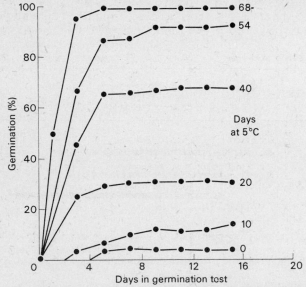

Fig. 6–2   Germination of excised apple embryos placed to germinate at 25 °C
after increasing periods of moist chilling (5 °C) as intact seeds (LUCKWILL, L. C.
(1952). *J. Hort. Sci.*, **27**, 53)

genetic dwarfing, which is an inherited condition. The symptoms can
be relieved by chilling the stunted seedling at 5 °C, or by its exposure
to long-day illumination, and thus in Nature such a condition would
be relieved sooner or later. It should be pointed out that if seeds from
commercially-purchased apples are used in laboratory experiments on
germination, it may be found that they will germinate without chilling
because this type of fruit is usually kept in cold storage for a time before
sale in the shops.

6.2.5   Combinations of dormancy types

It is frequently found that more than one type of dormancy may be
possessed by the same seed, which then needs more than one treatment

to cause germination. The European ash tree produces dry, single-seeded fruits which do not open to release the seed. This fruit shows a very deep state of dormancy in which germination does not occur until at least the second growing season after the fruit is shed from the tree. Although the embryo is fully formed it requires to grow to double its original size within the seed before germination, and embryo growth can only occur when the fruit has become imbibed either in the soil or in the ground surface litter. However, the growth of the immature embryo is slowed down by the fruit coat which restricts the entry of oxygen into the seed. Thus embryo growth is very slow until the outer layers become at least partially decayed. Even when the embryo is fully grown, it is still dormant, and cannot emerge from the seed until it has

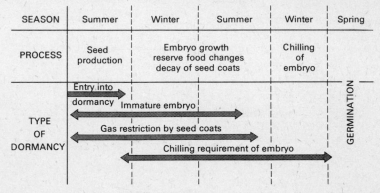

Fig. 6–3 Diagram of the combination of types of dormancy-imposing mechanism in the European ash tree, showing their relationship to the special timing of seed germination (data of VILLIERS, T. A., and WAREING, P. F. (1964). *J. Exp. Bot.*, **15**, 359)

been chilled at about 5 °C for at least 4 months (Fig. 6–3). Thus, the necessity for embryo development and the restriction of oxygen are probably responsible for preventing germination in the first spring, completion of the chilling requirement takes place in the second winter and germination then occurs in the second spring after production by the parent tree. Germination is sometimes delayed much longer than this depending on the initial rate of decomposition of the fruit coat and the total period of chilling achieved during the second winter.

6.2.6 Secondary dormancy

Seeds otherwise germinable may be caused to become dormant by imbibing them in unfavourable environmental conditions. This state of secondary dormancy can be relieved by the methods already described, such as chilling or exposure to light. Thus lettuce varieties which do not normally require light for germination can be induced to become light-requiring by imbibing them at temperatures above 30 °C.

In the next section, the imposition of secondary dormancy on the seeds of certain weeds associated with arable land is described.

6.3   Seeds in the soil

The major crop plants do not possess deeply dormant seeds, and when sown in the soil they usually germinate within a short time. This is probably because they have been selected over the centuries for precisely this property. Seeds in Nature require to have built-in devices which gauge an appropriate time for germination according to the seasonal cycle whereas Man can judge the best time to suit himself, according to his experience. It is usually found that seeds of plants only recently domesticated may still possess elaborate dormancy mechanisms which require some knowledge and trouble to overcome. Such is the case with forest trees, which have only recently come under systematic cultivation.

The seeds of wild plants may remain dry in the soil either because of their impermeable seed coats, or because they inhabit areas with seasonal or only occasional rain. However, in temperate climate areas, most seeds remain in the soil either continuously or intermittently fully imbibed, and yet do not germinate either until some requirement is completed, e.g. a minimal period of chilling, or in the case of weeds of arable land, until the soil is disturbed by cultivation. It has been shown that the original germination requirements of many such seeds may change so that they now require a different set of conditions before they will germinate. The seeds of many arable land weeds may require only a short period of drying out when freshly produced by the parent plant, and may therefore germinate within a short time if conditions are favourable. However, if conditions are not immediately favourable, e.g. if the seeds become buried by surface litter or by mechanical cultivation, they develop a state of secondary dormancy in which they now require exposure to light before germination can take place. They may then remain in the soil for variable lengths of time before some kind of disturbance, such as ploughing, brings them to the surface once more. There are several published accounts of seeds being dug up from under the turf of grassland which many years previously had been cultivated land, and a large proportion are usually still alive and can be germinated. Farmers find that on ploughing up previously cultivated grasslands, weeds typical of the last crop-associations on the land immediately begin to grow. Such weeds of cultivation have been described as 'opportunists' which achieve success in this man-created environment by means of such dormancy mechanisms. Seeds can also remain dormant in natural habitats for long periods, e.g. where the sunlight is filtered by a leafy canopy overhead, seeds on the forest floor not only have a greatly reduced light intensity, but the colour of the light is also changed (Section 9.1). Such seeds may germinate either when the leaf canopy dies and falls, when an old tree falls and leaves a gap, or after a forest fire.

At first sight it seems difficult to understand how such seeds can remain alive in the soil even though they do not germinate. In the first place they must resist attack by the soil micro-organisms, and they

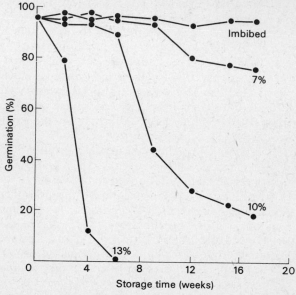

Fig. 6–4 Germination as tests of the viability of lettuce seed samples previously stored air-dry at a range of moisture contents (7%, 10% and 13%) compared with a sample of seeds stored fully imbibed with water (in the dark to prevent germination). Each point on the four curves represents the result of a separate germination test conducted after the storage time shown on the horizontal axis of the graph. (VILLIERS, T. A. (1974). *Plant Physiol.*, **53**, 875)

appear to be able to do so provided that they remain entire and un-damaged. Germination is prevented by one or another dormancy mechanism, but dormancy does not necessarily prevent all cellular activities. It has been shown that dormant imbibed seeds can respire, and can carry out protein synthesis in the formation of various cellular organelles and membranes. There is little doubt, therefore, that such seeds can also undertake at least some of the cellular repair and maintenance activities which are part of the normal metabolism of all tissues. On the other hand, dry-stored seeds are probably unable to repair damage, which must therefore accumulate and finally render the dry seed non-viable. Most of us think of seeds as they are stored at the seed merchants, and it comes as a surprise to find that seeds which are imbibed not only live longer than air-dry seeds (Fig. 6–4), but also accumulate much less genetic damage. Dry storage is still the most convenient method of keeping and transporting seeds, and under the most carefully controlled conditions of humidity, temperature and atmosphere, this method can keep seeds alive successfully for long periods. However, this is very artificial, and such conditions are not found in Nature. Seeds kept at equilibrium with the ordinary atmospheric humidity usually live for only a short period of time, and 'dry storage' in Nature is the exception rather than the rule.

7 Metabolism During Dormancy

Many aspects of metabolism have been studied during dormancy-breaking in the hope of obtaining explanations for the various types of dormancy. Information on the changes in enzymes and their activities is valuable, but it is very difficult to decide whether such changes are the cause or merely one of the effects of the relief of dormancy. Many changes certainly do occur during dormancy and it seems to be essential to view the process as a whole in order to obtain a full explanation of dormancy control. Modern theories of the control of growth processes suggest that the fundamental changes which occur may lie in the capacity of the genetic material to produce certain key enzymes or hormones, and that this activation of the genes often occurs in response to environmental signals. It is possible that different groups of organisms exert control over their growth and dormancy cycles at different stages of a common sequence of metabolic events.

7.1 Respiration and the dormant state

When seeds imbibe water, a sharp rise in respiration rate occurs, but if the seeds are dormant respiration later falls to a low level (see Fig. 7–1). Following treatment to break dormancy, the respiration rate again rises sharply in seeds requiring illumination in order to germinate, and more slowly in seeds requiring chilling. It has been suggested many times that dormancy may be a result of the interference of seed coats and bud scales with gas exchange. Enzyme activities might not be totally prevented, but if insufficient oxygen is available, certain biochemical pathways might be switched from those allowing normal growth to those preventing growth. However, it is unlikely that restriction of oxygen supply can be the cause of entry into dormancy of terminal shoots, since the switching of the developmental pathways into preparations for dormancy must occur before the bud scales are formed. In the seed, the embryo is entirely enclosed at all stages of its development and so an interference with oxygen supply could occur, at first from competition by the living maternal tissues for the inwardly-diffusing oxygen and later by these tissues developing into impervious layers.

Many seeds are stimulated to germinate if they become slightly damaged. Thus, seeds of birch germinate if their coats are merely scratched. However, it is found that the restricting effect of seed coats on gas exchange is usually accompanied by other factors imposing dormancy, and it is unlikely that restriction of the oxygen supply prevents germination or bud break solely by limiting the energy available for growth. In the case of birch seed, exposure to light and also chilling are effective in dormancy-breaking and it was shown that the stimulation of germination by seed coat damage is probably due to the removal of germination-inhibiting hormone by oxidation processes, whereas chilling and light may cause the production of counter-balancing germination-promoting hormones.

It has been suggested that the effect of low temperatures in breaking dormancy can be explained if it is considered in conjunction with the restriction of oxygen supply by the seed coats. At warm temperatures the rates of reaction will be high, and the seed may suffer from a shortage of oxygen causing certain metabolic pathways to be changed. However, if the seed is maintained at temperatures of about 5 °C, the rate of chemical reactions will be greatly slowed down and the amount of oxygen

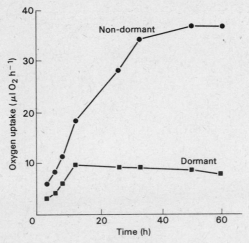

Fig. 7–1 Respiration rates of non-dormant (after-ripened in dry storage) and dormant seeds of wild oats in a germination test at 21 °C (CHEN, S., and VARNER, J. E. (1970). *Plant Physiol.*, **46**, 108)

diffusing inwards might now be sufficient to allow a diversion of these pathways back to those allowing growth.

It has been shown by E. H. Roberts that chemical inhibitors which block the tricarboxylic acid cycle of respiration (Kreb's cycle) are effective in breaking the dormancy of barley seeds. Respiration became diverted into the pentose phosphate pathway, which was shown to be required for normal germination of barley seeds. Barley does not require chilling before germination, but the dormant seeds will germinate at temperatures below 10 °C. Low temperatures have been shown to increase the activity of the pentose phosphate pathway in the embryos of other species.

The accumulation of carbon dioxide within the seed as a result of respiration, or in the soil as a result of microbial action, has often been suggested as a reason for dormancy imposition. However, in those cases where CO_2 has been shown to inhibit germination experimentally, the concentrations required are much higher than the levels of CO_2 found in the soil. In addition, a high CO_2 concentration has the effect of breaking dormancy in some cases rather than imposing it. It appears that an increase in CO_2 is unlikely to be a primary cause of dormancy, but may be one of a complex of factors generally affecting the metabolism of dormant tissues.

7.2 Reserve food changes

The breakdown of reserve food materials begins soon after uptake of water in a quiescent seed, and the biochemical events leading to these

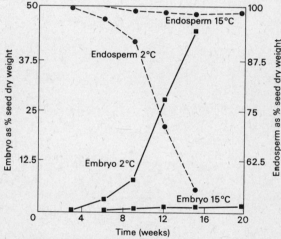

Fig. 7–2 The transport of materials from endosperm to embryo during moist chilling as a dormancy-breaking treatment in seeds of hogweed. The curves show the changes in weight of the embryos and endosperms of imbibed seeds stored at 5 °C, and at 15 °C (STOKES, P. (1952). *Ann. Bot.*, **16**, 441)

metabolic changes are described in Section 9.3. Even in a dormant seed, slow metabolism occurs resulting in the production of new substances, or in the re-distribution of reserve foods. During chilling of seeds of the hogweed, reserve food materials are transported from the endosperm into the embryo, which grows to twice its original volume and twelve times its original dry weight during the two months taken to relieve dormancy (Fig. 7–2). In fresh newly-formed embryos of the ash tree, a great deal of the stored food reserve is present as oil, but during dormancy this is largely removed and the amounts of carbohydrates and proteins increase. However, whereas these changes can be caused to occur when the seeds are imbibed at normal temperatures, dormancy is still not broken unless the seeds are chilled. The reserve food changes and the production or mobilization of the enzymes concerned are therefore probably part of the preparation for the early growth stages of the germinating embryo rather than being a major factor in the breaking of dormancy.

7.3 Phosphate metabolism

Owing to the connection between phosphorus and the transfer of energy in metabolism, it has long been considered that the availability of phosphate compounds may be of importance in dormancy control. More recently the importance of the nucleic acids in the storage and read-out of genetic information and therefore in the control of metabolism has been realized and there is renewed interest in the conversions of phosphates, especially the nucleoside phosphates, as precursors of the synthesis of the nucleic acids, DNA and RNA. In addition to the nucleic acids and free nucleoside phosphates, phosphorus also occurs in the cells of dormant organs as sugar phosphates, phytin, and phospholipids.

In cherry embryos held at warm temperatures, inorganic phosphates accumulate in the cells, whereas during chilling in order to break dormancy, phosphate is transported from the cotyledons and appears in the embryo axis as sugar phosphates, high-energy nucleotides (Fig. 7–3), and nucleic acids. Physiological studies have shown that there is also an increase in respiration rate and in the efficiency of the respiratory enzyme systems. It has been concluded that dormancy in cherry is at least partly concerned with blocking the metabolism of phosphorus. It is very difficult to decide whether such changes in

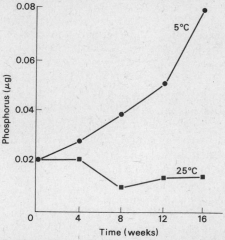

Fig. 7–3 The effect of moist chilling as a dormancy-breaking treatment on the levels of nucleotide high-energy phosphorus in cherry embryos. It can be seen that chilling increases the amount of high-energy phosphorus available for growth (OLNEY, H., and POLLOCK, B. M. (1960). *Plant Physiol.*, **35**, 970)

metabolism are the cause or merely one of the effects of dormancy breaking, but the connection of phosphate metabolism with the synthesis of nucleic acids, and therefore protein metabolism, seems to be a promising line of investigation.

7.4   Nucleic acid changes in dormancy

The overall process of chemical information storage and retrieval and its possible relationship to the control of dormancy are discussed in Section 8. The nucleic acids are concerned with the storage of genetic information (DNA) in the nucleus of each cell, and with the read-out (RNA) of this information and its use in protein synthesis. During

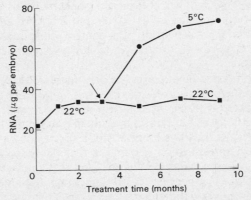

Fig. 7–4   Increase in total RNA of embryos of European ash during moist chilling as a dormancy-breaking treatment. All seeds were kept imbibed at 22 °C for the first 3 months in order to allow the immature embryos to develop fully. At this time, one batch of seeds was placed to chill at 5 °C (arrow). Further increase in RNA occurred only in the chilled sample (VILLIERS, T. A. (1972). New Phytol. **71**, 153)

treatments breaking dormancy in seeds (Fig. 7–4) and shoots, it is usually found that there is an overall increase in the total nucleic acids in the tissues and therefore an increase in the capacity for protein synthesis. Measured by the incorporation of radioactive substances into the nucleic acid fraction of the cells, RNA synthesis in hazel embryos increases during chilling, and the enzyme system responsible for RNA synthesis also increases in activity. Gibberellic acid is a hormone which breaks dormancy and is involved in seed germination (Section 8.4) and its application to unchilled hazel embryos causes the same increase in enzymes and RNA and also allows germination without the need for chilling. Application of the same hormone to ash embryos also stimulates the formation of RNA and permits germination, while the addition of abscisic acid, a hormone thought to be concerned in dormancy imposition, slows down the production of RNA (see Fig. 8–10).

8 Biochemical Controls and Dormancy

Great advances have been made in recent years in the biochemistry of protein metabolism. Proteins are the working molecules of living things, and are present in all cells as structural molecules and also as enzymes, without which very few reactions in cell metabolism could take place. This section gives a brief description of events in protein synthesis, and reviews some evidence that the regulation of dormancy stages in the life cycle might be achieved through gene activation and the control of protein synthesis.

8.1 The mechanism of protein synthesis

The material containing the information for the inherited characteristics of an organism is now accepted to be DNA. It is assumed that this genetic material also contains the developmental programme which sequentially unfolds the various stages of the life cycle of an organism. DNA is a long chain molecule built up from smaller units known as nucleotides. The sequence of these nucleotides along the chain is specific to the organism, and is ultimately responsible for the order of assembly of amino acids into proteins, which are therefore also specific to the organism. There is strong evidence that copies of the DNA chain are made by complementary matching with new nucleotides to form a

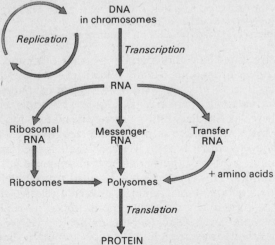

Fig. 8-1 Functional relationships between the various classes of nucleic acids in the process of protein synthesis

mobile (and disposable) copy of the DNA called messenger RNA (mRNA). This copying process has special requirements, including the presence of a specific enzyme called RNA polymerase.

Ribosomes are small, discrete particles made up of protein and ribosomal RNA (rRNA). They can be seen in the electron microscope and are postulated to become associated with the mRNA during the formation of protein. Whereas the mRNA provides the information for making a particular protein, the ribosomes are not specific, but apparently serve as organelles allowing the correct orientation between the nucleic acid and enzyme components of the system.

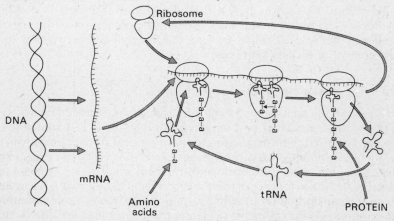

Fig. 8–2 A general scheme for the process of protein synthesis. Messenger RNA is formed as a chain of nucleotides complementary to one strand of the DNA. Ribosomes associate with this mRNA and serve to orientate the tRNA–amino acid molecules, together with the necessary enzymes, in the formation of protein molecules (a–a represents an amino acid)

Proteins are long-chain molecules consisting of amino acids connected in a linear order, and usually folded into a three-dimensional structure after their formation. Whereas RNA can be made from DNA by nucleotide matching (there are special rules about this which do not concern us here), amino acids cannot merely be matched to the nucleotides in the mRNA, as there is no specific recognition between such units. Instead, yet another type of RNA molecule is used in the activation of the amino acids and their alignment in sequence in the mRNA-ribosome complex. This type of RNA is called transfer RNA (tRNA) because of its function, and is a small molecule relative to the other classes of RNA. There is a different type of tRNA molecule for each of the twenty amino acids used, and the amino acid-tRNA bond is the same in each case. However, each tRNA type contains a short sequence of nucleotides which matches up with complementary sequences along the mRNA molecule. In this way the lack of specificity between mRNA nucleotides and the different amino acids is overcome, but different enzymes (tRNA synthetases) are needed to match up each amino acid with its specific tRNA molecule. There are other enzymes and cofactors concerned in the system and a supply of energy is required.

During active protein synthesis the ribosome moves relative to the long mRNA molecule, and it has been found that as one ribosome moves along from the beginning of the mRNA 'message', another ribosome can follow it. During active protein synthesis, a ribosome connects to the beginning of the mRNA as one leaves the end of the message, and therefore several protein chains may be formed at the same time. This assembly of several ribosomes on the same mRNA molecule is called a poly-ribosome, or polysome.

The process can be seen to be very complex indeed, but falls into two distinct stages. The first stage is concerned with the read-out of the information in the DNA to make a copy in the form of mRNA, and is called the 'transcription' process. The second stage occurs at the ribosome, and involves the formation of the protein chain of amino acids according to the mRNA sequence, and mediated by the tRNA. This is called the 'translation' process. Thus we have:

$$\text{DNA} \xrightarrow{\text{Transcription}} \text{RNA} \xrightarrow{\text{Translation}} \text{PROTEIN}$$

8.2 Control of protein synthesis

As the whole of cellular metabolism depends upon enzymes, which are proteins, then it might be suggested from the above description that metabolism could be stopped by blocking the read-out of the DNA at the transcription stage, or a selected metabolic pathway could be blocked by 'switching off' certain parts of the DNA and so preventing the formation of one or more enzymes specific to that pathway. However, even if the DNA does not produce more of a particular mRNA (message), there will still be molecules of this mRNA in the cell working in conjunction with ribosomes and therefore capable of continuing the production of a now-unwanted enzyme. In the bacteria it is found that mRNA is being continuously destroyed and new mRNA is formed to replace it, i.e. that there is a rapid 'turnover' of mRNA. As transcription control is an important means of metabolic control in the bacteria this rapid turnover is necessary.

In higher organisms there is some doubt about whether transcription control is used in the same way as a means of modulating protein synthesis. Large portions of the DNA of a mature cell are in fact not being used at all, and therefore not being transcribed. From the remaining fraction which is capable of being transcribed, mRNA is produced and its read-out may be controlled at the translation stage. It may be thought that the blocking of large portions of the DNA is the same as transcriptional control in the bacteria, but the difference lies in the fact that starting from a fertilized egg, which is a single cell, many cells are produced by division and become differentiated to perform very different functions. Therefore all cells come to possess a complete copy of the total genetic information (genome) but use only a small part of it, the rest being more or less permanently switched off.

Bacteria are single cells which use almost the whole of their genome, and have a very short lifespan with hardly any developmental programme at all when compared with multicellular organisms. mRNA is far more stable in higher organisms than in the bacteria, and there appears instead to be a higher rate of turnover of proteins. Several very ingenious schemes have been worked out to account for the control of protein synthesis at the translational stage, and which at the same time allow for the unfolding of stages of a developmental system of pro-

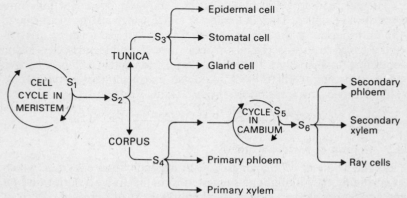

Fig. 8–3 A simplified, hypothetical scheme for the development of various types of stem tissue cells from a basic cell type (meristem cells) by a series of 'switches' (S1, S2, etc.) selecting different parts of the common genetic material

gressive changes in the patterns of enzymes formed. However, although there must obviously be some complex system of stage-by-stage progression in development with the possibilities of selection of a variety of possible pathways of differentiation, there is as yet little evidence for any particular scheme.

In summary therefore, at the transcription level there may occur masking of the DNA, and blocking of RNA polymerase. At the translation level we may find masking of the mRNA, blocking of ribosome function, absence or blocking of one or more types of tRNA, and absence or inhibition of one or more of the translation enzymes. Chemical inhibitors of various stages of protein synthesis have been of great use in experiments on the role of protein synthesis in various physiological processes. Two important and widely-used inhibitors are actinomycin D, which prevents RNA synthesis from DNA, i.e. transcription, and puromycin, which interferes with protein chain formation at the translation level.

8.3 Biochemical controls in the dormant state

From the previous section it can be seen that except in those species of plants possessing a purely physical method of imposing dormancy, such as the prevention of water uptake by seed coats, control of dormancy could be exerted through the modulation of protein synthesis. Dormancy is usually closely connected with complex morphogenetic processes such as bulb, tuber, winter bud, and seed formation, and also involves changes in the pattern of metabolism in an organ. Because in many cases the dormant state is involved in distinct developmental stages in the life cycle which require genetic information, and because pathways of development or metabolism are switched and therefore may require different enzymes, it is logical to assume a connection with the genome, and therefore with mechanisms controlling its activities.

The first level of control would be at the site of the genome itself, where the genetic material is selectively repressed or de-repressed according to the developmental pattern of the cell or organism. It is assumed that in response to stimuli or signals from the environment, such as daylength, the DNA may be in some way de-repressed and become capable of being transcribed, resulting in the formation of mRNA. This level of control, triggered by environmental signals, has been shown to occur in animals in the insect dormancy state called diapause. Subjection of dormant pupae of the silkworm to increasing daylength results in the production of a hormone called ecdysone, which causes emergence from diapause. Application of the synthetic hormone without photoperiodic treatment also causes emergence from the dormant state. The chromosomes of the salivary glands of other insects, such as the fruit fly, are very large and can be studied under the microscope. Application of ecdysone to the pupae can be shown to induce a repeatable and recognizable sequence of bulges, called 'puffs', on these chromosomes. Through various tests these puffs have been shown to consist of RNA, and are thought to be visible evidence of the activity of the DNA in producing mRNA. It is noteworthy that the same puffing sequence occurs when the pupae emerge from dormancy naturally.

This type of visible evidence is not available in the case of plants, but evidence for the masking of DNA and its consequent inactivity during dormancy has been presented by D. Tuan and J. Bonner, who experimented on the activity of extracted chromatin (the nuclear DNA with its associated protein) from dormant potato tubers. When the tubers were treated with ethylene (Section 8.4, dormancy could be broken and the buds ('eyes') began to grow. Chromatin extracted from dormant tubers was unable to take part in the formation of RNA in biochemical experiments, whereas chromatin extracted from tubers emerging from dormancy either naturally or after ethylene stimulation could act as a template (pattern) for the formation of RNA. The presence of actinomycin D, an inhibitor of DNA-directed RNA synthesis

(Section 8.2), prevented the formation of RNA by chromatin extracted from potato tubers treated with ethylene in order to break their dormancy. It was therefore suggested that dormancy in the potato tuber is maintained by the DNA being made unavailable for messenger RNA formation, and that the breaking of dormancy involves the controlled reactivation of the DNA by selective unmasking. Figure 8–4 shows the results of a similar type of experiment performed with hazel seeds, where gibberellin was used to break dormancy.

At the level of translation control there is evidence that in certain seeds the mRNA responsible for protein synthesis in translation is

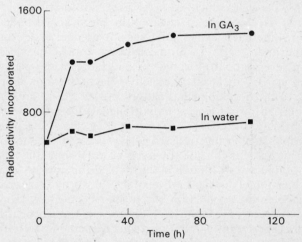

Fig. 8–4   Template activity (i.e. function of the DNA as a 'pattern' molecule) of chromatin (DNA plus its associated protein) extracted from embryos of hazel seeds placed in gibberellic acid in order to break dormancy. Activity of the chromatin was measured as the amount of radioactive nucleotide precursor incorporated into RNA (JARVIS, B. C. *et al.*, (1968). *Plant Physiol.*, **43**, 1734)

already present in the dry seed before water is imbibed. Experiments have shown that ribosomes extracted from dry wheat seeds are unable to make protein whereas those extracted from imbibed seeds are able to do so (Fig. 8–5). That the ribosomes from the dry seeds are functional can be shown by the addition of a synthetic 'messenger' RNA, polyuridylic acid, and therefore the ribosomes extracted from the dry seeds are not attached to mRNA. However, because wheat seeds are able to undergo protein synthesis leading to germination even if actinomycin D is present, it has been concluded that pre-formed mRNA must be present in dry wheat seeds, and upon imbibition this is made available to the ribosomes in some unknown way, after which protein synthesis begins the various metabolic sequences leading to germination. In addition to wheat, the seeds of lettuce and cotton also germinate in solutions containing actinomycin D.

Objections to these results have been that the actinomycin may not penetrate the cells sufficiently quickly to prevent transcription in the very early stages of imbibition, and secondly that there are indications that actinomycin might not be so effective in blocking DNA-directed RNA synthesis as is usually assumed. If the mRNA is produced in the embryo during the formation and maturation of the wheat seed, there must be some means of safely storing this in the cells in order to prevent its destruction and also to prevent its immediate use in protein synthesis.

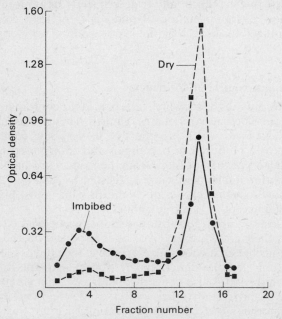

Fig. 8–5   Changes in the status of ribosomes after uptake of water by wheat embryos. The extracted ribosomal material was separated into size classes by high-speed centrifugation, and in the figure the polysomes decrease in size from left to right, with the two high peaks representing single ribosomes. Note that the increase in the quantity of polysomes in imbibed embryos is accompanied by a corresponding decrease in quantity of single ribosomes (MARCUS, A. (1969). In *S.E.B. Symposium No. 23*, Cambridge University Press)

This would therefore be an example of the control of the translation process by preventing the read-out of the mRNA.

Information on the various biochemical aspects of dormancy is accumulating slowly, and the examples given here are chosen to give some idea of the possibilities of dormancy control at the biochemical level. However, the impression which might emerge from the foregoing discussion may again be misleading. It should not be thought that dormancy is simply a stop-start mechanism dependent upon some particular biochemical activity being suspended for a time. Such an occurrence is only one aspect of a very complex sequence of events. It has already been stated that the initial changes following reception of the environmental signal may be those responsible for the switching of developmental pathways by repression and de-repression of the DNA. Thus in a shoot apex, extension growth may be stopped and vegetative leaves give way to the production of bud scales, or the same stimulus may lead to the formation of a tuber or a bulb before dormancy is imposed. Other events may follow, either as part of the sequence of DNA-directed activity occurring in sequentially-triggered steps, or as more superficial consequences of the formation of bud scales or seed coats causing changes in metabolism such as the suppression of an oxidative pathway.

8.4   Hormonal control of dormancy

Hormones are substances which take part in the coordination of functions between different parts of an organism. They are usually specific chemical substances which are effective in very low concentrations, most frequently produced in one organ and transported to exert an effect in other organs at a distance from their site of production. Chemical coordination in plants was first suggested in 1880 by J. Sachs, and there are now some five classes of chemicals which most plant physiologists would accept as plant hormones.

The auxins resemble the substance indole acetic acid either chemically, or in their growth effects. Auxin is produced in the stem apex and is responsible for a wide range of effects, including especially stem cell elongation and the directional responses of plants to light and gravity (tropisms). It is also concerned with xylem differentiation, fruit development and certain other processes. There is no evidence to suggest that the auxins are directly concerned in the control of dormancy.

The gibberellins are mainly concerned with stem elongation, which can be demonstrated in biennials, e.g. cabbage stem elongation, and promotion of the elongation of the stems of genetically dwarfed plants. Gibberellins are concerned with release from dormancy, and have been shown to increase in amount during winter chilling and after dormancy-breaking photoperiodic treatments.

The cytokinins are adenine derivatives and as such are related to the nucleic acids. They affect primarily cell division in plants, thereby affecting growth in all parts of the plant. They interact with other hormones such as auxin in producing growth effects, for example in the control of morphogenesis in tissue cultures, and in apical dominance in the intact plant. Cytokinins appear to interact with gibberellins and abscisic acid in controlling dormancy, for example in light-requiring seeds.

Abscisic acid is more directly concerned with the morphogenetic and biochemical changes leading to the imposition of dormancy, in which it is usually considered to interact with the gibberellins and probably also the cytokinins. It is also concerned with leaf and fruit abscission, and with the senescence of plant organs.

Although ethylene is a gas, it probably acts as a hormone in solution. It is concerned with many effects on plant growth, especially interacting with auxin, and is thought to be produced in tissues where the auxin concentration is high. It is especially effective in fruit ripening, and in

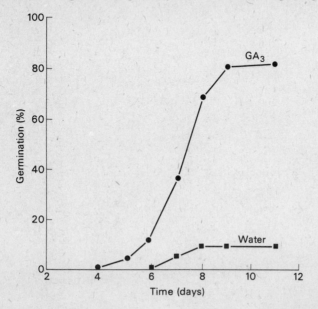

Fig. 8–6 The effect of gibberellic acid in stimulating the germination of dormant seeds of hazel (JARVIS, B. C. *et al.*, (1968). *Planta*, 83, 257)

senescence, and has the property of breaking dormancy, being very effective in the case of buds and other vegetative organs such as tubers and bulbs. It has also been implicated in the germination of seeds, for example, of lettuce.

8.4.1　Hormones and dormancy

It has become generally accepted that dormancy in higher plants is controlled by the balance between hormones which impose dormancy and hormones which stimulate active growth, although they may in fact be acting upon separate systems. In section 5.1 the physiology of winter bud formation is described and constitutes an excellent example of hormonal control. In response to a photoperiodic stimulus, abscisic acid

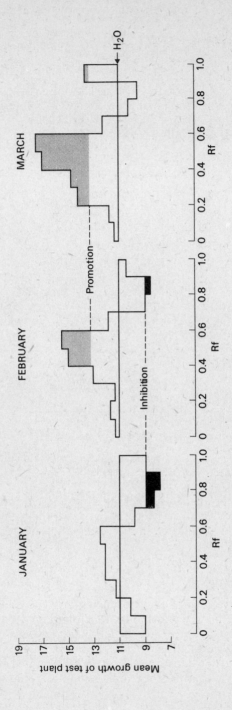

Fig. 8–7 Reduction of growth inhibitor (black areas) and increase in growth-promoting substances (shaded areas) in buds of black-currant during winter chilling. Hormone activity was measured by separating bud extracts by chromatography and assaying their effects on test plants (WAREING, P. F. (1969). In *S.E.B. Symposium No. 23*, Cambridge University Press)

is formed in the mature leaves and is transported to the shoot apex. Here it causes the primordia to develop into bud scales instead of vegetative leaves and prevents the internodes between these scales from extending so that the successive scales are able to form a tightly-enveloping protective sheath. Following this period of bud scale formation, the newer primordia develop once more into miniature vegetative leaves or floral parts which remain within the bud during winter. The whole process can be induced to occur even in good growth conditions in long-day illumination by the application of the purified hormone to the plants through the leaves, which under long days would not themselves produce abscisic acid.

The winter buds require to undergo a minimal period of chilling, i.e. to experience winter conditions, before they begin extension growth once more. The chilling effect can be replaced by long-day illumination, ensuring that growth will take place later in the season even after an excessively mild winter has been experienced. It has been shown that during chilling and long-day illumination there is an increase in the amounts of substances causing extension growth and which are similar to gibberellins and cytokinins when tested for their growth effects. The activities of the dormancy-inducing and growth-inducing hormones have been shown to vary relative to each other at different parts of the annual growth cycles of whole plants, and also in seeds. The dormancy-inducing hormones predominate in short days and the growth-inducing hormones predominate after receipt of the various environmental stimuli for growth. This kind of relationship has been shown for several plants, including the blackcurrant (Fig. 8–7).

There are many similarities between bud and seed dormancy which may not be at once obvious. It has already been described how winter buds forced into growth without sufficient chilling show rosette growth in which the leaves grow out but the stem does not extend, giving a telescoped appearance to the shoot. This condition may be relieved by long-day photoperiods or by the application of gibberellin. Similarly if embryos excised from unchilled, dormant seeds are forced to germinate and grow, they produce a rosette of leaves on a dwarfed stem, giving an appearance similar to that of a first-year biennial plant. This dwarf condition can be relieved by the application of gibberellin or by exposure to long days (see Fig. 5–3). Biennial plants which possess telescoped stems in the first year of growth and elongate after winter chilling can be induced to elongate at any time even in the first year of growth if gibberellin is applied. Gibberellin stimulates the germination of both light-requiring and cold-requiring seeds, and if used to force cold-requiring seeds to germinate without chilling, prevents the development of the symptoms of physiological dwarfing. It is not surprising therefore that gibberellins have been shown to appear in seeds during winter chilling.

The presence of a wide variety of growth-inhibiting substances has been shown in seeds, many of which may not actually play a major part in dormancy control as such, but may incidentally impose an environment generally unfavourable for growth until they may be reduced in quantity by diffusion in the soil water and adsorption to the soil colloids. However, abscisic acid has been identified in several seeds, such as American ash and rose seeds, and has been shown to decrease in amount during chilling. In other species, the inhibitor may not actually be removed by chilling, but may be overcome by a rise in the concentration of promoters such as the gibberellins.

It is therefore probable that seed dormancy is controlled by an interaction between dormancy- and growth-inducing hormones in the same

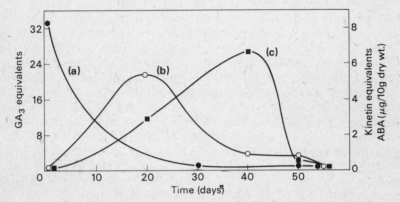

Fig. 8–8 Changes in hormone levels in seeds of sugar maple during chilling at 5 °C as a means of breaking dormancy. (a) Abscisic acid; (b) Cytokinins; (c) Gibberellins (WAREING, P. F., et al., (1973). Seed Ecology, Butterworths, London)

way as in buds. An interesting example of an interaction between hormones in the control of dormancy has been suggested by A. A. Kahn. Some varieties of lettuce seeds require light before germination when they are freshly harvested. The variety 'Grand Rapids' does not germinate in the dark, but will do so if gibberellin is applied in solution. If abscisic acid is administered at the same time, gibberellin is unable to promote germination even if present in excess, and therefore these hormones do not act by directly antagonizing each other. Cytokinin does not cause germination in the dark, but when given along with a mixture of gibberellin and abscisic acid, germination is permitted. As it does not reverse the inhibitory effect of abscisic acid by itself, but only if gibberellin is present, cytokinin has been suggested to exert its effect by nullifying the effect of the abscisic acid, so that when gibberellin is supplied, germination is then possible. It was suggested that this three-cornered system of interaction may operate in other species of plants and other types of organ.

Thus, in this view, dormancy would be imposed and maintained by abscisic acid, treatment to break dormancy would cause cytokinin to be formed, neutralizing the effect of the inhibitor, following which gibberellin would cause the extension growth necessary to begin the next growth cycle. There is good evidence of the involvement of all three hormones in the breaking of dormancy in cold-requiring seeds, such as the sugar maple, where it has been shown that chilling reduces the level of abscisic acid, and causes first an increase in cytokinin, followed by an increase in gibberellin before germination is possible (Fig. 8–8).

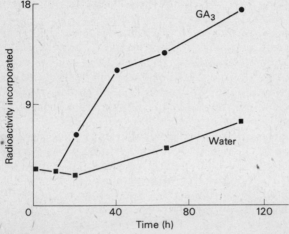

Fig. 8–9   Changes in the activity of RNA polymerase in embryos of hazel treated with gibberellic acid in order to break dormancy. This enzyme system is concerned in transcription from the genetic material (DNA) and is here measured as amounts of radioactive nucleotide RNA precursor incorporated per unit of DNA (JARVIS, B. C., *et al.*, (1968). *Plant Physiol.*, **43**, 1734)

8.4.2   Primary action of plant hormones

Although a great deal is known about the physiological effects of plant hormones in dormancy, their primary action at the biochemical level is not known. Attempts have been made to demonstrate the induction of particular enzymes in animals through the action of their hormones on the nucleic acid metabolism, and therefore on protein synthesis. In many cases an increase in RNA synthesis can be shown following hormone application which occurs before an increase in enzyme activity, but there appears to be no direct evidence that the DNA is specifically transcribed in response to the hormone, or whether the increase in RNA merely denotes a general rise in metabolic activity.

The same is true of biochemical experiments on plant dormancy. Gibberellin causes an increase in RNA polymerase activity and in RNA levels in hazel embryos (Fig. 8–9), and this is preceded by an increase in the reactivity of DNA in supporting RNA transcription. Gibberellin may therefore act directly or indirectly on the DNA, making it more available for transcription, and allowing the various enzymes responsible for growth to be produced. There is little doubt, however, that gibberellin has its effect upon nucleic acid activities, either directly or indirectly, as shown by its induction of the formation of the enzyme amylase during barley seed germination (Section 9.3). One interesting suggestion is that hormones such as gibberellin act upon cell membranes, causing them to change their properties of selective permeability.

Abscisic acid inhibits the formation of DNA and RNA in a variety of organs, both dormant and non-dormant, but it is perhaps unlikely that it maintains dormancy by preventing DNA synthesis as seed germination and bud burst usually begin before DNA synthesis and cell division occur. Inhibition of RNA formation could prevent the production of the enzymes necessary for stimulating extension growth and metabolism.

Cytokinins are derivatives of adenine, one of the bases occurring in the nucleic acids, and have been shown to be present in the molecule of transfer RNA. This has given rise to speculation on the possibility of a direct action of this type of hormone on protein synthesis, which could be modulated at the translation stage by the availability of types of tRNA. However, the evidence for such a direct action is inconclusive.

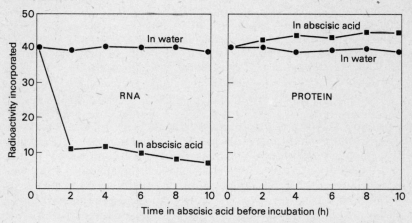

Fig. 8–10   Effect of abscisic acid on RNA (left) and protein synthesis (right) in excised European ash embryos germinating at 22 °C. The incorporation of radioactive nucleotide and amino acids was detected by autoradiography of embryo tissues (VILLIERS, T. A., (1968). *Planta*, **82**, 342)

9 Emergence from Dormancy

9.1 Environmental factors in dormancy-breaking

Seasonal changes in environmental conditions are responsible for controlling the cycles of growth and dormancy in plants and for the timing of seed germination, probably through the agency of hormone-like substances. The possession of mechanisms allowing environmental changes to be detected and timed is essential if plants are to survive in the majority of climatic areas, but while responses must be efficient, they must also be sufficiently variable or adaptable to allow for fortuitous variations of the weather. Additionally such variability would allow selection of new genotypes permitting the spread of plants into other climatic zones, and also enable them to adapt to survive long-term changes of climate.

9.1.1 Response to drying

The phenomenon of after-ripening of seeds in dry storage has been discussed in Section 6.2.2. While this requirement is an important consideration for agriculture-based industries, it is of vital necessity to plants inhabiting areas with periodic dry seasons. The majority of seeds become reduced in water content while they are on the parent plant, and even if they are dispersed while there is still sufficient soil moisture available for germination, they remain dormant until the completion of their minimal period of dry after-ripening. The seeds of winter annuals described in Section 1.3 are good examples of this type of dormancy. When freshly produced, they will not germinate under normally favourable conditions, but only at very cool temperatures. As the period of dryness progresses they pass from this state of deep dormancy to a state of relative dormancy, during which they become germinable at gradually increasing temperatures, and ultimately will germinate at warm temperatures after dormancy is completely broken (Fig. 9–1). It is not known what causes this change in dormancy characteristics, but it is unlikely to be hormonal in the first instance.

A difficulty arises in desert areas subject to infrequent and irregular rains. A light fall of rain might allow the germination of those seeds which have completed their dry after-ripening requirement, but might not be sufficient to support the growth of the plant produced. It has been shown that germination of such desert flower seeds only occurs after a heavy rain even though a light rain might have been sufficient to allow the seeds to become imbibed. It is thought that light rains are insufficient to wash out inhibitors of germination which occur in the seed coats, but that if continued rain falls for a period, the inhibitor concentration becomes sufficiently reduced by leaching to allow germination, and the extra-long rain provides sufficient water to soak the soil and allow plant growth to continue long enough to flower and set more seed.

9.1.2   Temperature effects

Apart from the obvious effect of temperature upon the rate of growth as a factor controlling the rates of chemical reactions, temperature affects germination in various ways. The germination of winter annuals

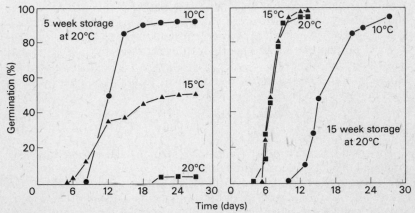

Time (days)

Fig. 9–1   Change in optimum germination temperature in seeds of the winter annual *Veronica arvensis* as a result of after-ripening in dry storage. Fresh seeds (left) germinate better at lower temperatures (10 °C), whereas after a period of dry storage good germination is attained at a wide range of temperatures, but is now more rapid at 15 °C–20 °C (data from JANSSEN, J. (1973). *Oecologia*, **12**, 141)

at cool temperatures, described above, ensures that while seeds produced in early summer do not germinate and so meet the dry season, seeds produced in autumn can germinate immediately and the seedling will be able to survive because of the sufficiency of rain and winter sunshine in the climatic regions which they inhabit.

The requirement for chilling of seeds and buds is characteristic of plants inhabiting the so-called temperate zones, where adverse, cold winters are experienced. The requirement ensures that seeds and buds do not begin growth until the winter is past. This mechanism has been described in Section 8.4 as an example of hormone-controlled dormancy. The total chilling requirement is usually increased by the presence of covering structures, such as seed coats, bud scales and the scale leaves of other dormant organs such as corms (see Fig. 9–2).

Germination conditions in the field are very different from those usually used in the laboratory, and temperatures fluctuate both diurnally and seasonally. Daily alternations of temperature are beneficial to plant growth and may often promote the germination of seeds which otherwise remain dormant if held at the same temperature continuously. The effect of alternating temperatures on germination is obscure, but several explanations have been suggested, including the need for the synchronization of various endogenous rhythms of metabolism which may occur in seeds.

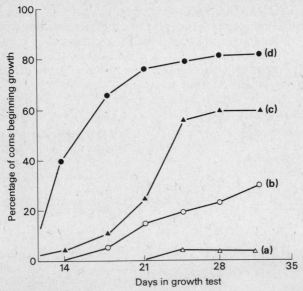

Fig. 9–2 The dormancy-breaking effects of chilling, and of removal of leaf scales from corms of *Gladiolus*. (a) Untreated corms, stored at 25 °C for 3 months; (b) Stored at 25 °C, scales removed for growth test; (c) Chilled at 6 °C for 3 months; (d) Chilled for 3 months, scales removed for growth test. The growth of corms was tested by placing on moist sand at 25 °C (GINZBURG, C. (1973). *J. exp. Bot.*, **24**, 558)

9.1.3   Light

The wavelengths of light promoting seed germination are in the red region of the spectrum (660nm). Far-red irradiation at 730nm inhibits the germination of light-stimulated seeds, as well as other morphogenetic processes controlled by light in plants. Whether germination will occur depends upon the wavelength of the irradiation last received by the seeds. However, if sufficient time is allowed to elapse between successive irradiations, it is found that far-red cannot re-impose dormancy, as the seeds have 'escaped' its effects.

It is accepted that a pigment, called phytochrome, is converted from one energy state to another and that when seeds are exposed to red radiation it is converted from P_{660} to the P_{730} form, and in this form is able to initiate certain reactions which ultimately cause germination. Exposure to far-red irradiation converts the pigment back to the P_{660} form, which is of a lower energy status and cannot take part in reactions. When sufficient time elapses between red and far-red irradiation to allow the seeds to escape the reversal effect of the far-red, it is presumed that the P_{730} has had time to begin the necessary reactions, which then become self-continuing.

Sunlight contains both red and far-red illumination, but is as effective as red light illumination in the promotion of germination because the reaction converting the pigment from P_{660} (the inactive form) to P_{730} requires only about one-quarter of the energy of its re-conversion by far-red. At the end of a period of sunlight, therefore, most of the pigment is present in the active form.

Light sensitivity can be induced in seeds if they are kept imbibed under unfavourable conditions in the laboratory and apparently also

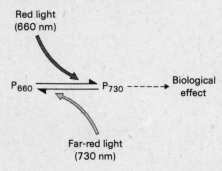

Red light
(660 nm)

P_{660} ⇌ P_{730} -----> Biological effect

Far-red light
(730 nm)

Fig. 9–3 Diagram showing the changes in state of the light-sensitive pigment phytochrome and its connection with growth and dormancy. P_{660} is activated by red light and converted to P_{730}, in which form it is able to initiate many physiological and morphogenetic processes. It slowly reverts to the inactive P_{660} spontaneously in the dark, but is rapidly re-converted by exposure to far-red light

in the field, and this is apparently an important factor in the adaptation of arable land weeds to their particular ecological niche (Section 6.3). Light sensitivity is also of value in dormant organs in sensing the quality of illumination in the environment, as a cover of plant leaves overhead alters the wavelengths of light available by acting as a spectral filter. When light passes through a canopy of leaves, the red light is absorbed by the chlorophyll and the illumination filtering through contains only a low percentage of red light. This effect can be demonstrated in the laboratory by using light passing through leaf material in germination experiments, when seeds will remain dormant. This may therefore be responsible for germination control in deciduous forests, or even under herbaceous plant cover, where many seeds germinate in early spring before the leaves have formed a canopy, and also for the large number of seedlings which appear in a forest clearing.

Phytochrome may bring about its effect via the formation of substances which de-repress the genome and allow the formation of hormones stimulating growth, such as the gibberellins. It has also been suggested to cause changes in cell membranes which alter the permeability of cells and allow the movement of substances initiating metabolism. A similar explanation has been offered for the effect of light in regulating dormancy in certain animal tissues.

9.2 Bud break and outgrowth

Although the terminal bud of a woody plant may appear very inactive, it is nevertheless capable of slow changes in internal morphology and in biochemical status. These changes consist of a slow continuation of development of the leaf and flower primordia within the buds, which has been shown to occur during winter in peach buds, and also changes in food reserves and the production of hormones such as the cytokinins and gibberellins. These changes probably do not occur at sub-zero temperatures, hence the importance of the minimal period of time required at temperatures around 5 °C. As the period of dormancy ends, the developmental process speeds up, and the buds swell visibly before finally the internodes elongate and push the bud scales aside during bud burst.

Although the primary function of the bud scales is no doubt protection, they actively inhibit growth of the internal parts in some species. It can be shown that they do not merely do this by interfering with respiration, because if the scales of unchilled winter buds of certain woody plants are pulled open to allow air access to the internal parts, these remain dormant. However, if the scales are actually cut off, growth may begin even in an unchilled shoot. The bud scales of peach tree have been shown to contain most of the growth-inhibiting substances detectable in the whole bud.

It has already been described how it is thought that dormancy in woody shoots is controlled by a balance between dormancy-inducing and growth-promoting hormones (Section 8.4), and it is assumed that growth begins after exposure to a certain number of cycles of gradually rising temperature when the level of growth-promoting hormones is above a certain threshold. It is interesting that although the stimulus to enter the dormant state may be transmitted throughout the plant from the site of reception of the stimulus, the breaking of dormancy in bud outgrowth is extremely localized. If even one branch of an overwintering tree is held inside a greenhouse through an aperture so that it does not receive its chilling requirement while the remainder of the tree is outside in normal winter conditions, the unchilled branch remains dormant even when the rest of the tree begins growth and produces leaves. However, it will begin to grow later in the season in long day photoperiods.

Many artificial treatments will cause the outgrowth of dormant buds, such as total immersion in warm water for a time, and also damage by wounding. Such treatments are mostly notable for their severity, and possibly may operate through a wounding stimulus to respiration and growth. Similar dormancy-breaking effects may be obtained by wounding overwintering animals such as insect pupae, where the stimulus is again considered to be a response to wounding by the stimulation of cell division and growth.

9.3   Seed germination

Germination is the activation of an embryo previously either quiescent or dormant. It usually begins almost immediately when a quiescent seed is placed in conditions suitable for growth, namely, at warm temperatures with water and air available. However, under such conditions the germination of a dormant seed may be delayed for long periods, and in some species may never occur at all unless special treatments are applied in order to break dormancy. Seeds of the ash tree have been kept imbibed for ten years in the author's laboratory, and cannot germinate unless they are chilled. Conversely, holding quiescent, non-dormant seeds under conditions of temperature and aeration unfavourable for growth may cause them to become dormant.

During treatments which break dormancy, seeds do not become non-dormant abruptly, but pass gradually through a period of relative dormancy during which they may germinate within certain limits of temperature. During treatment the range of temperatures within which germination can occur gradually becomes wider. After dormancy is broken, seeds of beech and ash are able to germinate from close to freezing point up to temperatures higher than 25 °C.

When dry, non-dormant seeds are placed in water, there is an initial phase of rapid water uptake during which the fresh weight of the seeds increases rapidly. This is followed by a period during which no further increase in weight occurs, after which water uptake begins again at a steadily increasing rate until there are visible signs of axis elongation. A wide range of metabolic processes must be initiated during the lag phase between the two stages of water uptake. One of the most important of these is the beginning of respiratory activity, but this may not be connected with the breaking of dormancy because dormant seeds also show an initial rise in respiration rate which later falls again to a low level (see Fig. 7–1). Respiration in imbibed seeds before germination has been shown to be largely anaerobic, probably owing to a restriction of oxygen supply by the seed coats.

Protein and RNA synthesis also begin during this lag phase, and most probably are concerned initially with the synthesis of enzymes for the mobilization of food materials and the formation of other substances in the preparation of the tissues for germination, which is the most active phase in the entire life of a plant. It has been shown that certain enzymes are absent from the mitochondria of dry seeds, and therefore these missing enzymes must be synthesized during early germination. Membrane synthesis occurs in the formation of systems of endoplasmic reticulum with attached ribosomes, and the Golgi bodies multiply and begin to produce large numbers of secretory vesicles. Electron microscope and biochemical studies show that shortly after a seed is stimulated to germinate, the ribosomes, which in the dry seed are present as monosomes, become aggregated to form polysomes. This is considered to be an indication that they have become associated with mRNA in the production of protein (Section 8.1).

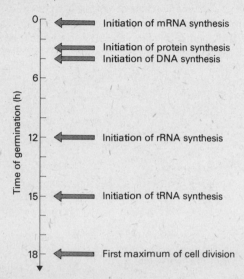

Fig. 9–4   The time sequence of the detection of some important biosynthetic processes during early germination of the wheat embryo. Zero time represents the beginning of water uptake. (DOBRZANSKA, M., et al., (1973). Nature, London, **244**, 508).

A most interesting system of new enzyme synthesis under the control of hormones has been worked out in detail in germinating seeds of barley (Fig. 9–5). The 'seed' (fruit) of barley has an embryo lying at one end, separated from the endosperm by a layer of tissue called the scutellum. The endosperm consists of dead cells with degenerated nuclei but packed with starch grains and protein granules. A thin layer of living cells called the aleurone layer surrounds this tissue, which constitutes the food supply of the system and must be mobilized to be made available to the embryo for its early growth.

During the early germination of the barley embryo the materials in the endosperm become liquefied and as the embryo grows, the food is transported from the endosperm into the embryo and utilized for its growth. If the embryo is removed from the seed before imbibition, no changes occur in the endosperm, and therefore the food breakdown must occur as a result of some influence from the embryo itself. However, replacement of the embryo on the endosperm, but separated from it by a dialysis membrane (which prevents the passage of macromolecules but not soluble molecules) allows the food digestion to occur apparently normally. This means that the enzymes necessary for the digestion do not come from the embryo, and it has been shown that they originate in the aleurone layer and pass into the endosperm.

After the discovery of the gibberellins as plant hormones, it was found that adding gibberellin alone to embryo-less barley endosperms causes the production of enzymes in the aleurone layer and the subsequent liquefaction of the food materials, even though they cannot be transported out because the embryo is missing. Hence, following water

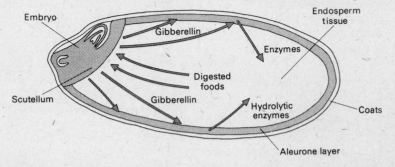

Fig. 9–5 Longitudinal section through a barley fruit, showing enzyme production by the aleurone tissue in response to a hormonal signal from the embryo (gibberellin). Products of the hydrolysis of the endosperm food materials are then passed to the embryo where they are utilized for germination and growth (After BLACK, M. (1972). *Control Processes in Germination and Dormancy*. Clarendon Press, Oxford).

uptake in the barley embryo, gibberellins must be synthesized or released. These move out to the aleurone layer, which becomes stimulated to produce a range of hydrolytic enzymes including amylase for starch digestion, proteases for protein digestion, and nucleases for nucleic acid digestion. These enzymes move into the endosperm, where sugars, amino acids and nucleotides are formed, and these food products move across into the embryo through the scutellum. It has been shown that most of these hydrolytic enzymes are not already present in the aleurone tissue and merely released, but are actually newly synthesized in response to the gibberellin. It is possible that similar methods of food mobilization occur in other types of seed, although it has been shown that in some seed, enzymes are activated from pre-existing zymogens rather than being synthesized *de novo*.

10 Conclusions

It is not known at what stages in the various metabolic systems the blocks to growth exist in dormant organs. Respiration can occur, although there is more than one respiratory pathway allowing the production of high-energy compounds. New cell membranes and organelles can be formed, and therefore protein synthesis must be able to take place, although perhaps at a slow rate. Food interconversions can occur and therefore there should be a supply of substrates. One turns therefore to the logical and attractive theory of the control of dormancy through the activities of the nucleic acids in protein synthesis. Selective repression of the DNA would allow a control of dormancy through the absence of one or more key enzymes which might directly or indirectly take part in extension growth, which is the visible result of the breaking of dormancy.

All the various structural modifications for dormancy must be produced ultimately from information encoded in the genome, the activities of which may be triggered either as part of an autonomous sequential programme, or by environmental signals. Synchrony of the organism with seasonal changes is essential. Therefore it is necessary for the plant to use an external signal at some stage in the annual cycle, but it has been shown in Section 2.3 that the only reliable rhythmic environmental signal is that of daylength.

The means of sensing light, and of timing its duration, is the phytochrome system, which is widely present in plants. One of the suggestions for the explanation of phytochrome action is that it may control membrane permeability, perhaps itself being part of a membrane system, and it is possible to consider selective membrane permeability as a means of modulating gene activity, or any metabolic process, through the control of the movements of activators, repressors, hormones or substrates from one membrane-bound compartment to another. The chilling process could also exert its effect through changing membrane permeability.

Thus, the state of dormancy and any structural modifications entailed are normal developmental stages in the life history which have been synchronized with the seasons, and are encoded in the genome. The synchronizer or trigger is an environmental signal perhaps achieving its effect through the regulation of membrane permeability. Changes in hormonal and physiological status, and the inhibition and activation of metabolic pathways, may be expressions of gene activity in the operation of the developmental programme and are probably mediated through RNA and protein metabolism.

Further Reading

BLACK, M. (1969). Light-controlled germination of seeds. In *Society for Experimental Biology, Symposium No. 23.* Cambridge University Press

KOZLOWSKI, T. T. (1972). *Seed Biology,* Vol. 2. Academic Press, New York.

LESHEM, Y. (1973). *The Molecular and Hormonal Basis of Plant-growth Regulation.* Pergamon Press, Oxford.

MARCUS, A. (1969). Seed germination and the capacity for protein synthesis. In *Society for Experimental Biology, Symposium No. 23.* Cambridge University Press.

PHILLIPS, I. D. J. (1971). *Introduction to the Biochemistry and Physiology of Plant Growth Hormones.* McGraw-Hill, New York.

ROBERTS, E. H. (1972). *Viability of Seeds.* Chapman & Hall, London. (Includes sections on dormancy.)

SMITH, A. (1973). *The Seasons.* Penguin Books, Harmondsworth, U.K.

THOMPSON, P. A. (1973). Geographical adaptations of seeds. In *Seed Ecology,* ed. W. Heydecker. Butterworths, London.

VEGIS, A. (1963). Climatic control of germination, bud break and dormancy. In *Environmental Control of Plant Growth,* ed. L. T. Evans. Academic Press, New York.

WAREING, P. F. (1969). The control of bud dormancy in seed plants. In *Society for Experimental Biology, Symposium No. 23.* Cambridge University Press.

WAREING, P. F. and PHILLIPS, I. D. J. (1970). *The Control of Growth and Differentiation in Plants.* Pergamon Press, Oxford.

WAREING, P. F., VAN STADEN, J. and WEBB, D. P. (1973). Endogenous hormones in the control of seed dormancy. In *Seed Ecology,* ed. W. Heydecker. Butterworths, London.

WILKINS, M. B. (ed.) (1969). *The Physiology of Plant Growth and Development.* (Includes sections on dormancy.) McGraw-Hill, London and New York.